C000017218

Key Stage 1

Science

Wendy Clemson

Text © Wendy Clemson 2001
Original illustrations © Nelson Thornes Ltd 2001

The right of Wendy Clemson to be identified as author of this work has been
asserted by her in accordance with the Copyright, Designs and Patents Act 1988.

All rights reserved. The copyright holders authorise ONLY users of *Learning
Targets Science Key Stage 1* to make photocopies of *pages 100-192* for their own
or their students' immediate use within the teaching context. No other rights are
granted without permission in writing from the publishers or under licence from the
Copyright Licensing Agency Limited. Further details of such licences (for
reprographic reproduction) may be obtained from the Copyright Licensing Agency
Limited, of 90 Tottenham Court Road, London W1T 4LP.

Copy by any other means or for any other purpose is strictly prohibited without
prior written consent from the copyright holders. Application for such permission
should be addressed to the publishers.

Any person who commits any unauthorised act in relation to this publication may
be liable to criminal prosecution and civil claims for damages.

Published in 2001 by:
Nelson Thornes Ltd
Delta Place
27 Bath Road
CHELTENHAM
GL53 7TH
United Kingdom

01 02 03 04 05 / 10 9 8 7 6 5 4 3 2 1

A catalogue record for this book is available from the British Library

ISBN 0 7487 3589 5

Printed and bound in Great Britain by The Bath Press

**Nelson Thornes publishes a comprehensive range of teacher resource books in the *Blueprints* and *Learning
Targets* series. These titles provide busy teachers with unbeatable curriculum coverage, inspiration and value
for money. For a complete list, please call our Primary Customer Services on 01242 267280, send an e-mail to
cservices@nelsonthornes.com or write to:**
Nelson Thornes Ltd, Freepost, Primary Customer Services, Delta Place, 27 Bath Road, Cheltenham GL53 7ZZ.
**All Nelson Thornes titles can be bought by phone using a credit or debit card on 01242 267280 or online by
visiting our website – www.nelsonthornes.com**

CONTENTS

Welcome to Learning Targets   4
Introduction   6
Curriculum Planners   8

Life Processes and Living Things   12

TOPIC 1   Being alive   12
TOPIC 2   You and me   14
TOPIC 3   Our senses   16
TOPIC 4   Body labels   18
TOPIC 5   Babies   20
TOPIC 6   Food   22
TOPIC 7   Being ill, getting better   24
TOPIC 8   Pets   26
TOPIC 9   Mini-beasts   28
TOPIC 10   Get moving!   30
TOPIC 11   What is a plant?   32
TOPIC 12   Plant labels   34
TOPIC 13   Let's grow   36
TOPIC 14   Plant babies   38
TOPIC 15   Matching alike/unlike   40
TOPIC 16   Looking at plants   42
TOPIC 17   Looking at animals   44
TOPIC 18   Grouping   46
TOPIC 19   Habitats   48

Materials and their Properties   50

TOPIC 20   Sensing   50
TOPIC 21   Is it magnetic or non-magnetic?   52
TOPIC 22   Transparency and other properties   54
TOPIC 23   Naming materials   56
TOPIC 24   What do we use it for?   58
TOPIC 25   Shape changes   60
TOPIC 26   Heating and cooling: changing back 62
TOPIC 27   Heating and cooling: all change   64

Physical Processes   66

TOPIC 28   Play safe   66
TOPIC 29   What does electricity make
           things do?   68
TOPIC 30   Making circuits   70
TOPIC 31   On the move   72
TOPIC 32   Push and pull   74
TOPIC 33   Speeding up, slowing down or
           changing direction   76
TOPIC 34   Road safety   78
TOPIC 35   Light toys   80
TOPIC 36   Light and darkness   82
TOPIC 37   Shadow play   84
TOPIC 38   Light sources   86
TOPIC 39   The sun, the Earth and the moon   88
TOPIC 40   Making noises   90
TOPIC 41   Hearing   92
TOPIC 42   Comparing sounds   94
TOPIC 43   What makes a sound?   96
TOPIC 44   Sound travelling   98

Copymasters 1–91   100–190
Record Sheet 1   191
Record Sheet 2   192

Welcome to

Learning Targets is a series of practical teacher's resource books written to help you to plan and deliver well-structured, professional lessons in line with all the relevant curriculum documents.

Each Learning Target book provides exceptionally clear lesson plans that cover the main concepts and ideas of its stated curriculum plus a large bank of carefully structured copymasters. Links to the key curriculum documents are provided throughout to enable you to plan effectively.

The Learning Targets series has been written in response to the challenge confronting teachers not just to come up with teaching ideas that cover the curriculum but to ensure that they deliver high quality lessons every lesson with the emphasis on raising standards of pupil achievement.

The structure of Learning Targets has been created to reflect what are currently seen as key imperatives in effective teaching. These include:

➤➤ that effective teaching is active teaching directed to very clear objectives

➤➤ that good lessons are delivered with pace, rigour and purpose

➤➤ that good teaching requires a range of strategies – including interactive whole class sessions

➤➤ that ongoing formative assessment is essential to plan children's learning

➤➤ that differentiation is necessary but that it must be realistic.

The emphasis in Learning Targets is on absolute clarity. We have written and designed the books to enable you to access and deliver effective lessons as easily as possible, with the following aims:

➤➤ to plan and deliver rigorous, well-structured lessons

➤➤ to set explicit targets for achievement in every lesson that you teach

➤➤ to make the children aware of what they are going to learn

➤➤ to put the emphasis on direct, active teaching every time

➤➤ to make effective use of time and resources

➤➤ to employ the full range of recommended strategies whole-class, group and individual work

➤➤ to differentiate for ability groups realistically

➤➤ to use ongoing formative assessment to plan your next step

➤➤ to have ready access to usable pupil copymasters to support your teaching.

The page opposite provides an at-a-glance guide to the key features of the Learning Targets lessons and explains how they will enable you deliver effective lessons. The key to symbols on the lesson plans is set out here. ➤➤➤

How to deliver structured lessons with pace, rigour and purpose

Explicit targets for achievement in every lesson

Detailed preparation notes including any health and safety issues

Crystal clear lesson plan layouts

Rigorous and practical activities

The full range of teaching strategies

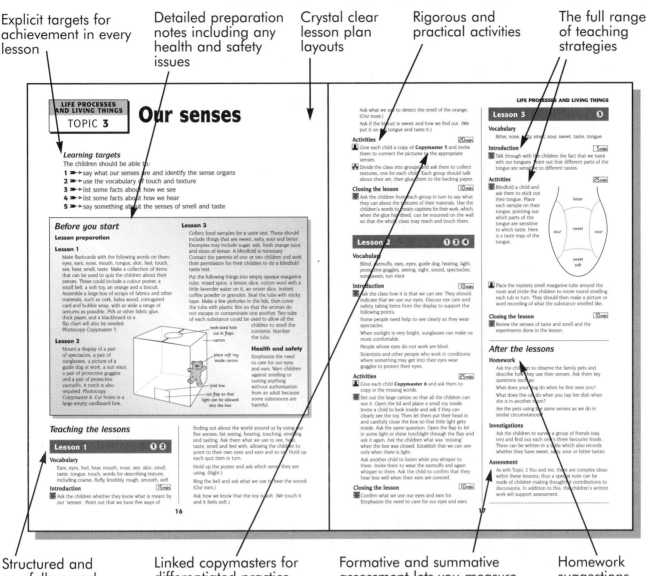

Structured and carefully paced lessons

Linked copymasters for differentiated practice and assessment

Formative and summative assessment lets you measure achievement against the targets – and plan the next step

Homework suggestions

The symbol key

③ Indicates the number of the Learning Target covered in each session or lesson

10min Suggested duration for each part of the session

Interactive whole class teaching session

Group work session

Individual within a group work session

Pair work session

Individual session

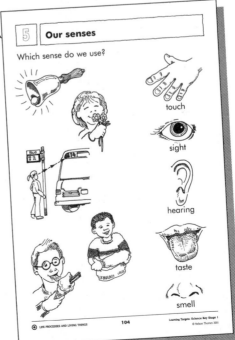

5

INTRODUCTION

Learning Targets for Science Key Stage 1 includes lessons on scientific concepts for children aged five to seven (Years R–2). Together with its companion book, *Learning Targets for Science Key Stage* 2, it offers support for the teaching of key concepts in science suitable for children in this age group. In planning and writing this book, the author has not only sought to meet the requirements of the National Curriculum for England (Curriculum 2000) and the 5–14 National Guidelines, Environmental Studies: Science (Scottish Executive) but has also taken note of the QCA/DfEE Science Scheme of Work.

This book is a foundation for science teaching. There are some lessons at each level of work appropriate for the Key Stage. It contains a series of well-structured, detailed and specific lesson plans, backed by linked copymasters, which you can use to teach lessons in line with the National Curriculum and the 5–14 National Guidelines. It is not intended, however, that this book and its companion volume should constitute a complete scheme. They supply a range of sample lessons which can be used for many science sessions at Key Stages 1 and 2.

As each of the two science books in the series addresses work at a whole Key Stage (either Years R–2/P1–3 or Years 3–6/P4–7), it is necessary to select topics and lessons at the appropriate level. You can use your own discretion in this or consult the chart on page 10 to match lessons to units in the QCA/DfEE Science scheme of work which have been assigned to specific years within the Key Stage. Within each topic, there are three lessons in which there is progression in learning and the lessons should, therefore, be taught in order.

How this book is organized

Topics

The topics do not have to be taken in order and it is preferable that they are not. The intention is that you should dip into the book, taking from it those lessons that are appropriate for the term or year in which your class is working. Where a cluster of linked topics occurs, it may prove appropriate to teach the lessons contained in the first of these before the lessons in subsequent ones. For example, it is educationally sound to introduce Topic 31 On the move before Topic 32 Push and pull, then Topic 33 Speeding up, slowing down or changing direction. Indeed it would be quite appropriate to tackle these topics terms or even years apart, provided this strategy fits the school science plans. Thus work on Topic 31 could be done in Year R, Topic 32 in Year 1 and Topic 33 in Year 2. The topics are, however, independent of each other. It is also possible for you to choose lessons from within a topic as independent lessons.

Within each topic, the lessons are sequenced to be more demanding as the children progress from Lesson 1 to Lesson 3. The Learning Targets state explicitly what the children should be able to do by the end of each topic. The Learning Targets provide you with a clear set of assessable objectives.

The lesson plans within each topic are very specific and detailed in their teaching suggestions, written to allow you to undertake direct teaching to clear objectives. There are suggested timings for each activity within a lesson, the total time for which has been set to around 45 minutes. This is because it is expected that this meets both the limitations set by a crowded timetable and the educational needs of young children.

Some lessons have accompanying copymasters, which are completely integrated into the teaching activities.

At the end of each topic, there is a section headed After the lessons which comprises the following:

Homework

There are some suggestions for information retrieval, recording and other scientific activities that the children can carry out at home.

Investigations

Here are some more open-ended activities, chosen particularly to give children opportunities in information retrieval and the use of secondary sources, hypothesizing, predicting, and experiment design, execution and modification. They also offer extension possibilities for more able children. Investigations should, however, form part of every child's experience of science education and space should be found for them within the science timetable.

Assessment

These are notes that give pointers concerning which elements of the children's work in the topic are most amenable to assessment scrutiny. You can differentiate between children's learning by the outcomes of their work.

National curricula and science

The lessons in this book have been written to match the time demands on teachers. The scientific ideas relate to the required range of work in National Curricula and those seen as important in the QCA/DfEE Science Scheme of Work.

Each topic can provide the material for a number of science lessons. We realize that every teacher will interpret the demands of the science curriculum individually in the light of their own situation. The structure of the book allows for this. In order to offer science lessons, it is suggested that you consult the topic titles to locate the lesson required at the appropriate time to allow planning before the session.

The Learning Targets for each topic have been matched with the Programme of Study in the National Curriculum for England (Curriculum 2000) and related to Units within the QCA/DfEE Science Scheme of Work. These charts are on pages 8–10.

The Learning Targets for each topic have also been matched with the statements in the Attainment Outcomes in Curriculum and Assessment in Scotland, 5–14 National Guidelines, Environmental Studies, Science. This chart is presented on page 11. Teachers in Scotland can therefore be confident that the lessons in this book meet the requirements to which they are working.

As curricula are constantly under review, please visit our website at www.nelsonthornes.com for the latest guidelines.

SC1   Scientific enquiry

Topic No.	1	a	b	c	d	e	f	g	h	i	j
1	●		●					●	●		
2	●		●				●	●	●		
3	●		●			●	●	●			
4			●					●	●		
5	●	●	●				●	●	●		●
6	●		●				●	●	●		●
7	●	●	●				●	●			
8	●		●			●	●	●			●
9	●	●	●				●	●	●		
10	●		●				●	●	●		
11	●		●				●	●	●		●
12	●		●				●	●	●		●
13	●	●	●		●		●	●	●		●
14	●		●				●	●	●		
15	●	●	●				●	●	●		●
16	●	●	●				●	●	●	●	
17	●		●				●	●	●		
18	●		●	●			●	●	●		●
19	●	●	●				●	●	●		●
20	●	●	●		●		●	●	●		
21	●	●	●		●		●	●	●		
22	●	●	●	●	●			●	●		●
23	●	●	●				●	●			
24	●	●	●	●	●	●	●	●		●	
25	●	●	●				●	●	●		
26	●	●	●				●	●	●		
27	●	●	●				●	●	●		
28	●		●				●		●		
29	●	●	●					●	●		
30	●	●	●				●	●	●		
31	●	●	●	●				●	●	●	
32	●	●	●	●	●	●	●	●	●		●
33	●	●	●	●	●	●	●	●			●
34	●		●				●	●	●		
35	●	●	●	●			●	●	●		
36	●	●	●				●	●	●		
37	●	●	●				●	●	●		
38	●	●	●				●	●			
39	●	●	●					●			
40	●	●	●				●	●	●		
41	●	●	●				●	●	●		
42	●	●	●				●	●	●		
43	●	●	●				●	●	●		
44	●	●	●				●	●	●		

SC2   Life processes and living things

Topic No.	1 a	1 b	1 c	2 a	2 b	2 c	2 d	2 e	2 f	2 g	3 a	3 b	3 c	4 a	4 b	5 a	5 b	5 c
1	●	●			●													
2		●		●										●				
3		●		●					●									
4				●														
5		●						●										
6		●			●	●												
7							●											
8		●	●	●	●			●								●		
9		●	●	●				●										
10		●																
11	●		●															
12			●													●		
13		●									●							
14		●											●					
15															●			
16			●									●						
17		●		●	●		●		●									
18															●			
19			●													●		●
20																		
21																		
22																		
23																		
24																		
25																		
26																		
27																		
28																		
29																		
30																		
31																		
32																		
33																		
34																		
35																		
36																		
37																		
38																		
39																		
40																		
41																		
42																		
43																		
44																		

SC3 Materials and their properties

Topic No.	1 a	1 b	1 c	1 d	2 a	2 b
1						
2						
3						
4						
5						
6						
7						
8						
9						
10						
11						
12						
13						
14						
15						
16						
17						
18						
19						
20	●					
21		●				
22		●				
23			●	●		
24		●		●		
25					●	
26						●
27						●
28						
29						
30						
31						
32						
33						
34						
35						
36						
37						
38						
39						
40						
41						
42						
43						
44						

SC4 Physical processes

Topic No.	1 a	1 b	1 c	2 a	2 b	2 c	3 a	3 b	3 c	3 d
1										
2										
3										
4										
5										
6										
7										
8										
9										
10										
11										
12										
13										
14										
15										
16										
17										
18										
19										
20										
21										
22										
23										
24										
25										
26										
27										
28	●									
29	●									
30		●	●							
31				●						
32				●	●					
33					●	●				
34				●	●	●				
35							●			
36								●		
37								●		
38							●			
39										
40									●	
41										●
42									●	
43									●	
44										●

Curriculum planners
QCA/DfEE Scheme of work: Primary Science

Topic No.	1A Ourselves	1B Growing plants	1C Sorting/using materials	1D Light and dark	1E Pushes and pulls	1F Sound and hearing	2A Health and growth	2B Plants/animals in the local environment	2C Variation	2D Grouping/changing materials	2E Forces and movement	2F Using electricity				
1	●	●														
2	●															
3	●					●										
4	●															
5	●						●									
6							●									
7	●						●									
8									●							
9								●								
10	●							●								
11		●														
12		●														
13		●														
14		●														
15									●							
16								●								
17								●								
18										●						
19										●						
20			●													
21			●							●						
22			●													
23			●													
24			●													
25										●						
26										●						
27										●						
28																
29												●				
30												●				
31											●					
32					●						●					
33											●					
34											●					
35				●												
36				●												
37				●												
38				●												
39				●												
40						●										
41						●										
42						●										
43						●										
44						●										

Curriculum planners
National Guidelines Environmental Studies 5–14 (Scotland)

ATTAINMENT OUTCOMES: SCIENCE LEVEL A AND LEVEL B

KNOWLEDGE AND UNDERSTANDING: EARTH AND SPACE

Earth in space	Changing materials
Level A Identify the Sun, the Moon and the stars *Topic* 39	**Level A** Make observations of the ways in which some materials can be changed by processes such as squashing, bending, twisting and stretching *Topic* 24
	Level B Describe how everyday materials can be changed by heating or cooling *Topics* 26, 27
Materials from Earth	
Level A Recognize and name some common materials from living and non-living sources *Topics* 23, 24 Give examples of uses of some materials based on simple properties *Topics* 23, 24	
Level B Make observations of differences in the properties of common materials *Topics* 20, 21, 22, 23 Relate uses of everyday materials to properties *Topic* 24	

KNOWLEDGE AND UNDERSTANDING: ENERGY AND FORCES

Properties and uses of energy	Forces and their effects
Level A Give examples of sources of heat, light and sound *Topics* 35, 36, 37, 38, 40, 41, 42, 43, 44 Give examples of everyday uses of heat, light and sound *Topics* 35, 36, 37, 38, 40, 41, 42, 43, 44 Give examples of everyday appliances that use electricity *Topics* 29, 30 Identify some of the common dangers associated with the use of electricity *Topic* 28	**Level A** Give examples of pushing and pulling, floating and sinking *Topics* 31, 32, 33, 34
Level B Identify the Sun as the main source of heat and light *Topics* 38, 39 Link light and sound to seeing and hearing *Topics* 35, 41	**Level B** Describe the effect that a push and pull can have on the direction, speed or shape of an object *Topic* 33 Describe the interaction of magnets in terms of the forces of attraction and repulsion *Topic* 21
Conversion and transfer of energy	
Level B Give examples of being 'energetic' *Topic* 31 Link the intake of food to the movement of their body *Topic* 31	

KNOWLEDGE AND UNDERSTANDING: LIVING THINGS AND THE PROCESSES OF LIFE

Variety and characteristic features	Interaction of living things with their environment
Level A Recognize the similarities and differences between themselves and others *Topics* 2, 4 Sort living things into broad groups according to easily observable characteristics *Topics* 15, 16, 17, 18	**Level A** Recognize and name some common plants and animals found in the local environment *Topics* 9, 12, 16, 17, 19 Give examples of how to care for living things and the environment *Topics* 8, 11, 13
The processes of life	
Level A Name and identify the main external parts of the bodies of humans and other animals *Topics* 4, 17 Describe some ways in which humans keep themselves safe *Topics* 3, 34 Give the conditions needed by animals and plants in order to remain healthy *Topics* 8, 13	
Level B Give examples of how the senses are used to detect information *Topic* 3 Recognize the stages of the human life cycle *Topic* 5 Recognize the stages in the life cycles of familiar plants and animals *Topics* 5, 14	

Being alive

Learning targets

The children should be able to:

1 ➤➤ list some of the things that show we are alive
2 ➤➤ name some living things and identify signs of life in them
3 ➤➤ name some non-living things
4 ➤➤ list some things humans need

Before you start

Lesson preparation

Lesson 1

Make up class-sized flashcards with picture and word signs on them, along with the following words and phrases: move, grow, breathe, go to the lavatory, eat. Photocopy Copymaster 1. Here are some examples of flashcards.

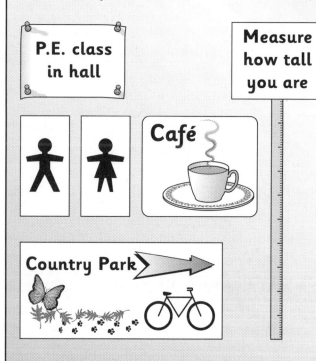

Lesson 2

The flashcards for Lesson 1 are required. Record a wildlife programme on video for the children to watch. Set up a display of non-living things which should be labelled; for example, rocks, pebbles, plastic toys, plastic kitchenware, metal spoons, metal forks, and clothing made from artificial fabrics such as polyester, nylon and viscose. These could be placed on a table in the corner of the room or be a temporary display on a tea tray and shown to the children at the appropriate point in the lesson. Anything made from something that was once living, such as wool or wood, for example, should be avoided, as these are 'dead' rather than 'non-living'.

Lesson 3

Use the display of non-living things used in Lesson 2. You may wish to add to it. Set up a doll's house with kitchen, bedroom and bathroom equipment, and evidence of a garden. Make available to the children a large quantity of construction apparatus, suitable for making rooms, people and so on (for example, Duplo® or Lego®). Photocopy Copymaster 2.

Investigations

Obtain video footage of plants growing to show to the children.

Health and safety

All living things, including the children themselves and plants, require care to preserve life. This is an opportunity to impress this upon the children.

Teaching the lessons

Lesson 1 ①

Vocabulary

Alive, breathe, eat, go to the lavatory, grow, move; words used on the flashcards; words used by the children in discussion

Introduction 〔10min〕

▦ Ask the children what they think it means to be 'alive'. Accept all their answers, including comments such as 'I can see', 'I can count', 'I can dance', 'I dream', 'I play'. Discuss some of the things they do that show they are live such as moving, growing, breathing, going to the lavatory, and eating. (If appropriate, also include the following characteristics: sensing – seeing, hearing, tasting, touching, smelling – and having babies, although these will be studied in later topics). Hold up and practise the words on the class flashcards.

Activities 　　　　　　　　　　25min

 Set up the class flashcards so that all the children can see them. Give each child a copy of **Copymaster 1** and invite them to draw two or more pictures of themselves doing things that show they are alive. Each child can write a caption word for each picture, using the flashcards, or you can write in the word for them to trace write with a pencil.

Put up the 'Café' sign. Invite two or three children to mime what goes on there. Ask the children to say what we all do in cafés, which indicate that we are alive; namely eat and drink. Point out that this is something all living things do. Now take each of the other signs in turn and allow the children to mime what the cards indicate. Here are suggestions.

Flashcard	Activities
PE class in hall	Children move and breathe
Measure how tall you are	Shows growth
Country park	Children walk, run and breathe
Boys/girls lavatory symbols	Fix this to the inside of the classroom door and ask each child to go through the door. Ask the class what they would be doing having gone through the door

Closing the lesson 　　　　　　5min

Remind the children of the key things that they all do that show they are alive. Point out that these are indicators of life for all living things.

Lesson 2 　　　　　　　　　②③

Vocabulary

The words on the flashcards used in Lesson 1; the names of the animals seen on the video along with the names of the non-living things on the display

Introduction 　　　　　　　　　5min

Remind the children of the characteristics that show they are alive, using the flashcards from Lesson 1. Tell the children that they should look for signs of life in other creatures while watching the video.

Activities 　　　　　　　　　　35min

Allow the children to watch about 10 minutes of the video you have selected. Talk through with them what the animals are called, what they are doing and the signs that show they are living creatures.

 Invite each child to draw or paint a living creature on a piece of paper. Ask them to write a caption for the picture that gives their reasons for saying that the creature they have drawn is alive. Alternatively, they may dictate the caption to you.

Draw the children's attention to the display of non-living things. Tell the children the meaning of 'non-living'. Ask key questions such as, for example:

Why do you think this rock is not alive?

Do any of these things breathe?

Closing the lesson 　　　　　　10min

Review, with the children's help, all the characteristics of living things that the children saw in the video.

Lesson 3 　　　　　　　　

Vocabulary

Words for human needs, for example, air, drink, food, love, rest, water; words the children use as required; the words on the flashcards made for Lesson 1 may be needed

Introduction 　　　　　　　　　5min

Put a non-living item next to one of the children. Ask the children to make comparisons between their classmate and the item in terms of what the live person can do and what the non-living thing cannot do.

Activities 　　　　　　　　　　30min

Give each child a copy of **Copymaster 2** and invite them to draw a non-living thing and match up the words to the appropriate pictures. Plants are included in the picture so that the idea that plants are also alive can be raised with the children.

Show the children the doll's house and point out the table, chairs and food in the kitchen. This is a reminder that humans need food. Ask the children what else humans need and draw from them the ideas that we need rest, air to breathe, space to move in, water to drink, and so on. Link our needs to life and health.

Divide the class into groups and ask the children to use the construction apparatus to create a model room with a person in it doing something connected with a human need.

Closing the lesson 　　　　　　5min

Examine the children's models and show them to the class. Allow some of them to say what the person in their model is doing.

After the lessons

Homework

Ask the children to name, draw and count the humans, pets and plants they can see living in their homes.

Investigations

Allow the children to watch video footage of plants growing, sensing and moving to establish that plants are alive.

Ask the children to list as many different living creatures as they can.

Assessment

Check the children's speaking, listening and writing skills and their participation in the class activities.

You and me

Learning targets

The children should be able to:

1 ➤➤ say what a human is and realize that humans are all alike
2 ➤➤ show that we differ from one another in some ways
3 ➤➤ list some ways in which humans are like other animals
4 ➤➤ list some human capabilities and some ways in which humans differ from other animals

Before you start

Lesson preparation

Lesson 1

Make some class-sized flashcards with the following words and phrases on them: head, body, two legs, two arms, hair, eyes, ears, nose, mouth. Also cut some blank flashcards. A flip chart or a blackboard may be useful. Cut enough lengths of thick wool for half the class and collect enough clean lolly sticks for the whole class. Magnifiers (one between two children) and felt-tip pens are needed. Photocopy Copymaster 3.

Lesson 2

Painting paper, paints and brushes as well as drawing materials are required. Assemble a collection of model animals (a farm, ark or zoo would be ideal). Include some model humans in the collection. Photocopy Copymaster 4. Enough pairs of scissors for half the class are needed.

Lesson 3

Large sheets of painting and drawing paper as well as paper with large squares on for chart-making are all needed.

Investigations

Paper with large squares on for chart-making may be required.

Teaching the lessons

Lesson 1   ① ②

Vocabulary

Body, ears, eyes, hair, head, mouth, nose, two arms, two legs; words the children use to describe themselves and others

Introduction   [10 min]

▦ Tell the children that we are human. Use 'human beings' and 'humankind' in explaining that we all belong to this group. Ask the children to try describing a human. Use the flashcards as appropriate, making new ones for the words the children use.

Activities   [30 min]

👤 Give each child a copy of **Copymaster 3** and invite them to colour the pictures that show that we are all human and alike.

▦ Bring the class together and point out that while we are all alike, there are some ways in which we differ from one another. Ask the children to identify differences such as hair colour and eye colour.

👥 Get the children to pair up. Using the magnifiers, the children can compare the skin pattern on their thumbs. They can each then mark up a lolly stick to show how the lengths of their index fingers compare. They can use the wool to measure each other's waists to see if there are differences in size. The wool can be marked with a felt-tip pen in a contrasting colour. The wool can also be used to measure the distance between fingertips when the arms are outstretched. It may be helpful to draw pictures to show all these challenges on the flip chart or blackboard so that the children can get on with their investigations while you circulate among them.

Closing the lesson   [5 min]

▦ Review the two Learning Targets of the lesson.

14

Lesson 2   ③

Vocabulary

The names of the animals to be used in the lesson

Introduction   5 min

▦ Tell the children that humans are animals and point out some of the ways in which humans are like other animals. Ask the children to add to the list of similarities between humans and some other animals. Relate these features to those common to all living things.

Activities   30 min

👤 Invite the children, either individually or in pairs, to
👥 paint and draw animals of their choice. When dry, these pictures can be mounted in a frieze round the room, with captions showing features they have in common with humans. Example pictures and captions are shown below.

This tiger uses its eyes to see

Kangaroos use their legs for hopping

Cats have a lot of hair called 'fur'

Looking after puppies

👥 Give each pair a copy of **Copymaster 4** and a pair of scissors. They can cut out the parts of the animals and create some strange creatures by putting them together differently. This activity should lead to a discussion of appropriate features.

Closing the lesson   10 min

▦ Gather the children round the model animal collection. Ask a child to place an example of each kind of animal in a group or pen. Check that a human is included and discuss this with the children.

Lesson 3   ④

Vocabulary

Capabilities, features, play, read, swim, write and other words the children use

Introduction   10 min

▦ Allow each child to tell the class about something they think they are especially good at. They may, for example, say that they play the recorder, swim, read or write well. Write on the board or a flip chart a list of their capabilities. Point out that these are all things humans can do. Other animals can do some of them but not all of them.

Activities   25 min

👥 Divide the children into pairs. Ask them to draw something that they themselves are good at, then next to this or on a similar piece of paper draw something that their partner is good at. Ask the children to choose capabilities that are different from their partner's. Invite them to write underneath the appropriate pictures 'I am good at . . .', 'My friend is good at . . .'.

♣ Divide the children into groups and while the other children watch, invite each group to mime an activity that humans do, then say whether they think other animals do this activity.

Closing the lesson   10 min

▦ Point out to the children that humans have special features that enable them to have capabilities that other animals do not have. These include the size and complexity of our brains, our ability to use language which comes from this, and the fine co-ordination in our hands.

After the lessons

Homework

Ask the children to list or draw 20 things they do on a Saturday which demonstrate human capabilities.

Investigations

Invite the children to observe and report the hair or eye colours of people in their family.

Ask the children to draw themselves and one of their pets or another animal alongside them, then draw lines to connect things that are similar about the two of them.

Ask the children to collect pictures of people from magazines; these can be made into a class collage and could even have the outline of a row of people as shown below; captions created by the children can be added.

Pictures of people cut from magazines

Assessment

There are complex ideas within these lessons; thus a special note can be made of children making thoughtful contributions to the discussions. In addition to this, the children's written work will support assessment.

Our senses

Learning targets

The children should be able to:

1 ➡➤ say what our senses are and identify the sense organs

2 ➡➤ use the vocabulary of touch and texture

3 ➡➤ list some facts about how we see

4 ➡➤ list some facts about how we hear

5 ➡➤ say something about the senses of smell and taste

Before you start

Lesson preparation

Lesson 1

Make flashcards with the following words on them: eyes, ears, nose, mouth, tongue, skin, feel, touch, see, hear, smell, taste. Make a collection of items that can be used to quiz the children about their senses. These could include a colour poster, a small bell, a soft toy, an orange and a biscuit. Assemble a large box of scraps of fabrics and other materials, such as cork, balsa wood, corrugated card and bubble wrap, with as wide a range of textures as possible. PVA or other fabric glue, thick paper, and a blackboard or a flip chart will also be needed. Photocopy Copymaster 5.

Lesson 2

Mount a display of a pair of spectacles, a pair of sunglasses, a picture of a guide dog at work, a sun visor, a pair of protective goggles and a pair of protective earmuffs. A torch is also required. Photocopy Copymaster 6. Cut holes in a large empty cardboard box.

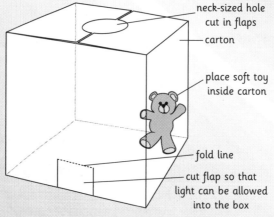

neck-sized hole cut in flaps

carton

place soft toy inside carton

fold line

cut flap so that light can be allowed into the box

Lesson 3

Collect food samples for a taste test. These should include things that are sweet, salty, sour and bitter. Examples may include sugar, salt, fresh orange juice and slices of lemon. A blindfold is necessary. Contact the parents of one or two children and seek their permission for their children to do a blindfold taste test.

Put the following things into empty opaque margarine tubs: mixed spice, a lemon slice, cotton wool with a little lavender water on it, an onion slice, instant coffee powder or granules. Seal the tubs with sticky tape. Make a few pinholes in the lids, then cover the tubs with plastic film so that the aromas do not escape or contaminate one another. Two tubs of each substance could be used to allow all the children to smell the contents. Number the tubs.

Health and safety

Emphasize the need to care for our eyes and ears. Warn children against smelling or tasting anything without authorization from an adult because some substances are harmful.

Teaching the lessons

Lesson 1 ① ②

Vocabulary

Ears, eyes, feel, hear, mouth, nose, see, skin, smell, taste, tongue, touch; words for describing texture, including coarse, fluffy, knobbly, rough, smooth, soft

Introduction 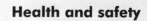 ⬚15 min

▓ Ask the children whether they know what is meant by our 'senses'. Point out that we have five ways of finding out about the world around us by using our five senses; list seeing, hearing, touching, smelling and tasting. Ask them what we use to see, hear, taste, smell and feel with, allowing the children to point to their own eyes and ears and so on. Hold up each quiz item in turn.

Hold up the poster and ask which sense they are using. (Sight.)

Ring the bell and ask what we use to hear the sound. (Our ears.)

Ask how we know that the toy is soft. (We touch it and it feels soft.)

Ask what we use to detect the smell of the orange. (Our nose.)

Ask if the biscuit is sweet and how we find out. (We put it on our tongue and taste it.)

Activities
`20min`

 Give each child a copy of **Copymaster 5** and invite them to connect the pictures to the appropriate senses.

 Divide the class into groups and ask them to collect textures, one for each child. Each group should talk about their set, then glue them to the backing paper.

Closing the lesson
`10min`

Ask the children from each group in turn to say what they can about the textures of their materials. Use the children's words to create captions for their work, which, when the glue has dried, can be mounted on the wall so that the whole class may reach and touch them. .

Lesson 2
① ③ ④

Vocabulary

Blind, earmuffs, ears, eyes, guide dog, hearing, light, protective goggles, seeing, sight, sound, spectacles, sunglasses, sun visor

Introduction
`10min`

Ask the class how it is that we can see. They should indicate that we use our eyes. Discuss eye care and safety, taking items from the display to support the following points.

Some people need help to see clearly so they wear spectacles.

When sunlight is very bright, sunglasses can make us more comfortable.

People whose eyes do not work are blind.

Scientists and other people who work in conditions where something may get into their eyes wear goggles to protect their eyes.

Activities
`25min`

Give each child **Copymaster 6** and ask them to copy in the missing words.

Set out the large carton so that all the children can see it. Open the lid and place a small toy inside. Invite a child to look inside and ask if they can clearly see the toy. Then let them put their head in and carefully close the box so that little light gets inside. Ask the same question. Open the flap to let in some light or shine torchlight through the flap and ask it again. Ask the children what was 'missing' when the box was closed. Establish that we can see only when there is light.

Ask another child to listen while you whisper to them. Invite them to wear the earmuffs and again whisper to them. Ask the child to confirm that they hear less well when their ears are covered.

Closing the lesson
`10min`

Confirm what we use our eyes and ears for. Emphasize the need to care for our eyes and ears.

Lesson 3
⑤

Vocabulary

Bitter, nose, salty, smell, sour, sweet, taste, tongue

Introduction
`5min`

Talk through with the children the fact that we taste with our tongues. Point out that different parts of the tongue are sensitive to different tastes.

Activities
`25min`

Blindfold a child and ask them to stick out their tongue. Place each sample on their tongue, pointing out which parts of the tongue are sensitive to which taste. Here is a taste map of the tongue.

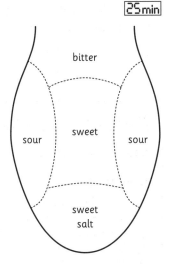

Place the mystery smell margarine tubs around the room and invite the children to move round smelling each tub in turn. They should then make a picture or word recording of what the substance smelled like.

Closing the lesson
`10min`

Review the senses of taste and smell and the experiments done in the lesson.

After the lessons

Homework

Ask the children to observe the family pets and describe how they use their senses. Ask them key questions such as:

What does your dog do when he first sees you?

What does the cat do when you tap her dish when she is in another room?

Are the pets using the same senses as we do in similar circumstances?

Investigations

Ask the children to survey a group of friends (say, ten) and find out each one's three favourite foods. These can be written in a table which also records whether they have sweet, salty, sour or bitter tastes.

Assessment

As with Topic 2 You and me, there are complex ideas within these lessons; thus a special note can be made of children making thoughtful contributions to discussions. In addition to this, the children's written work will support assessment.

Body labels

Learning targets

The children should be able to:

1 ➤➤ point to and name the main parts of the human body
2 ➤➤ read the names for the parts of the body
3 ➤➤ write the names for the parts of the body

Before you start

Lesson preparation

Lesson 1

You will need a life-sized body outline, felt-tip pens, card labels with body parts written on one side and sticky tape on the other side. Draw a body outline on a large sheet of paper or ask a child to lie on lining or sugar paper and draw around their shape with a felt-tip pen. Make up card labels for the following body parts: head, shoulder, neck, arm, leg, hand, foot, wrist, ankle, shin, thigh, elbow, fingers, toes, chest, tummy, back, bottom. Photocopy Copymaster 7.

Lesson 2

Collect pictures of people from magazines and advertisements. Make up instruction cards as illustrated on page 19. Photocopy Copymasters 7 and 8 and create some similar work sheets.

Lesson 3

You will need plane safety mirrors, word cards and word lists of parts of the body and face, including, for example, the words listed in the vocabulary.

Investigations

You will need pictures and video footage of mammals along with books about mammals, string, measuring tapes and measuring sticks, computers and CD-ROMs about the human skeleton.

Health and safety

Be sensitive to the issues around touching parts of the body. Use the session to discuss with the children the idea that they should take care of their bodies and try not to hurt themselves or others.

Teaching the lessons

Lesson 1 ① ②

Vocabulary

Ankle, arm, back, bottom, chest, elbow, fingers, foot, hand, head, knee cap, leg, neck, shin, shoulder, shoulder blade, spine, thigh, toes, tummy, wrist

Introduction ⎢5min⎢

▨ Call out the names of the parts of the body that you think the children will know and ask them to hold up, wave or point to the appropriate part of their own bodies. For example, ask them to 'Show me your arm', 'Show me your foot', 'Show me your head'.

Activities ⎢30min⎢

▨ Hang up the body outline and invite individual children to point out the parts that you name while the other children watch. Then ask one or two children to help you place the body part labels where they go on the outline. When all the labels are on the picture, point to each one and ask the whole class to say what it says.

 Give each child a copy of **Copymaster 7** and ask them to connect each label to the appropriate body part.

Closing the lesson ⎢15min⎢

▨ Remove the whole body outline from view. Hold up individual body part labels at random and ask individual children to read the labels aloud; try to give every child several turns.

Lesson 2 ① ② ③

Vocabulary

Ankle, arm, back, bottom, chest, elbow, fingers, foot, hand, head, knee cap, leg, neck, shin, shoulder, shoulder blade, spine, thigh, toes, tummy, wrist

Introduction

▦ Use pictures of people from magazines, advertising and posters to give the opportunity for volunteers to point to and name some body parts.

Activities

15 min

👤 Give the children outline figures like those on Copymaster 7 (additional copies of the picture from Copymaster 7 can be used) and some instructions on little cards, so that they read the names of the body parts and carry out the instructions as shown below.

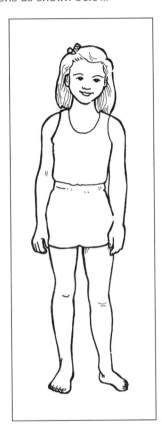

Colour the legs

Make the hands blue

Colour the head and hands pink

Give the children worksheets where they are required to write the names of body parts. **Copymaster 8** is an example. More labels can be added to this, and additional pictures of children in action can be used to create worksheets for the children to complete.

Closing the lesson

5 min

▦ Use the worksheets or copymaster from the above activity to remind the children of the label words they should be using.

Lesson 3   ① ② ③

Vocabulary

Adam's apple, cheek, chin, collar bone, ear, eyebrow, eyelash, eyelid, forehead, knee cap, lips, mouth, nose, nostril, shoulder blade, spine

Introduction

10 min

▦ Using a volunteer from the class, tell the children the names of the parts of the face. Give the children an oral quiz, using questions such as, for example:

What on your face is below your mouth?

On your face you have two cheeks; what else can you see on a human face, that comes in twos?

Write on the board the words the children use.

Activities

15 min

👥 Give each child a plane safety mirror and invite them to draw their own face, then show their picture to a friend and name the parts of the face in the picture.

Closing the lesson

10 min

▦ While the class watch, invite individual children to act out, for example, how a game is played or how the washing-up is done, naming the body parts they use for these activities as they go.

After the lessons

Homework

Allow the children to make a full-length drawing of themselves or one of their family and write in the names of some parts of the body from memory.

Ask the children to draw a portrait of a family member or their pet and label the picture.

Investigations

Look at pictures and video footage of other mammals and ask the children to try to identify the body parts. For example, ask them: 'Where are a cat's shoulders?' Help the children to research the information in books and other sources.

Ask the children to work in pairs to make measurements of parts of the body, using string, measuring tapes and measuring sticks.

Invite the children to compare the hands of people of different ages. They can, for example, carefully draw around the hand of a five-year-old, a ten-year-old and an adult. These can be cut out and set alongside one another. (For links with growth see Topic 5 Babies.)

Invite the children to find and look carefully at pictures of the human skeleton on CD-ROM. Ask the children to feel their own bodies gently to see if they can detect any of the bones.

Assessment

Check speaking and listening, taking part, and writing against the Learning Targets.

Babies

Learning targets

The children should be able to:

1 ➤➤ understand that babies grow into adults
2 ➤➤ understand that we do not go on growing throughout life
3 ➤➤ understand that babies and children change as they grow and adults change as they age
4 ➤➤ understand that babies and children are cared for by adults
5 ➤➤ recognize that young animals resemble their parents
6 ➤➤ understand that some creatures have several life phases

Before you start

Lesson preparation

Lesson 1

Ask the children to bring into school some family photographs. Be sure to obtain their parents' permission and ask an adult to write the child's name on the reverse of the pictures for identification. Mount a display of the photographs in the classroom. Invite people of a range of ages to call into the classroom for part of the lesson. It would be helpful if there is a child in the class whose family have a young baby and a toddler who could be brought in. Ask among the kitchen staff, caretakers, secretaries, crossing patrol staff and other school workers for volunteers to join an 'age identity parade'.

Lesson 2

Cut out about a dozen pictures of people from magazines. Include at least one person in the following age ranges: newborn, under one year, two–five, six–ten, twelve–fifteen, 16–25, 35–45, 50+, 80+. Try to include pictures that have clues to the age of the person; for example, a young mother with her child or a toddler with a push-along toy.

Assemble a resource bank of pictures of humans and other animals caring for their young.

Lesson 3

Model farm animals, pictures of these animals or access to real farm animals would be very helpful here; alternatively, if there are school pets these can be brought into the classroom. You will need access to a resource bank of books, CD-ROMs and videos about animal families and the life cycles of metamorphosing creatures (for example, the frog). Photocopy Copymasters 9 and 10.

Investigations

Use the secondary sources collected for Lesson 3. You will also need large sheets of paper (squared paper may be useful) for charts to collate the age data.

Health and safety

Be sensitive to the fact that some children do not live in households where both parents are present. Take care to observe the LEA/school guidelines with regard to children and live animals. Good hygiene, recognition of possible allergies, and appropriate handling and care of the animals are essential.

Teaching the lessons

Lesson 1   ① ② ③

Vocabulary

Adult, age, aunt, baby, brother, child, cousin, daddy, elder, eldest, father, granddad, grandma, mother, mummy, old, sister, stepfather, stepmother, teenager, uncle, young; other words the children use associated with the human life cycle and family relationships

Introduction   [5 min]

 Establish with the children the sequence in the human life cycle, from baby to child to teenager to adult. Check that they can describe this as a process of change over time.

Activities   [35 min]

 Show the children the display of family photographs. Ask them appropriate questions, for example:

Which of these two people is the elder? How do you know that?

What tells you this is a baby/the youngest person here?

Who is an adult? Point to one.

👤 Ask the children to draw their own families, placing people in order of their age.

▦ With the assistance of the invited people standing at the front of the class, ask the children questions, for example:

Who is the youngest person? How do you know?

Who comes next?

Which person here is aged about 20?

Who could be a grandma? Why do you say that?

Closing the lesson 5min

▦ Drawing attention to the visitors, point out their varying heights. Use this data to show that height is not necessarily associated with age and that adults have stopped growing in height.

Lesson 2

Vocabulary

Adult, age, baby, child, grow, height, old, short, tall, teenager, weight, young; other words the children use during the lesson

Introduction 5min

▦ To reinforce the work done in Lesson 1, ask the children the phases in the human life cycle.

Activities 30min

👤 Allow the children to walk round the room and inspect all the pictures of people. These should be numbered but not arranged in order of age and mounted on the wall at a level at which the children can look closely at them. The children can then list them in order of age on a piece of paper.

▦ Bring the class together and review the order in which the pictures should be placed. Point out specific clues in the pictures that tell us about the person's phase of life, such as whether they are able to walk, the relative sizes of their head and limbs, whether their skin is wrinkled, and so on. It may be that the children will see all grown ups as 'old' but it is important that they know that adults do change, even though they do not increase in height once adulthood is reached.

▦ Point out to the children that babies are looked after by adults. Ask them why this is and establish a list of tasks the adults do for the child. Discuss how the child gradually learns to be independent of adults. Draw attention to comparisons that can be made with the behaviour of other mammals. Show the children pictures of humans and other animals caring for their young.

Closing the lesson 5min

▦ Ask the children to mime for a moment being in turn a baby, themselves, a teenager and an adult.

Lesson 3 ⑤ ⑥

Vocabulary

The names of farm animals and their young

Introduction 15min

▦ Show the children some models and pictures of young animals. Ask volunteers to name them and pick out a matching adult from the model box or group of pictures. Point out that the animals all have young of the same kind as the parents – calves are born to cows and not sheep, for example. If there are school pets available these can be brought into the classroom and ideas about the young of these animals can be discussed.

Activities 35min

👤 Ask the children to complete **Copymaster 9**, connecting baby animals to their parents. They can then colour in the pictures, using pencils of the appropriate colours to match real live animals.

▦ Choose a creature which has several distinct life phases and discuss how and when the creature changes its appearance and life phase.

▦ Talk through **Copymaster 10** pointing out that all
👤 but the cat have distinct life phases. Then allow the children to colour in the creatures.

Closing the lesson 5min

▦ Review with the children the idea that humans and other mammals have babies that are like them and that there are creatures that have distinct life phases.

After the lessons

Homework

Ask the children to get help at home to assemble a timeline of photographs of themselves from newborn to their present age. These could be photocopied and displayed in the classroom for the children to see.

Investigations

Ask the children to collect the names of baby animals and the corresponding adults; for example, a baby deer is a fawn and its parents are a buck and a doe.

Ask the children to find the answers to age-related questions among family members; for example, the ages at which the people in the family start school, begin to read, change schools, move house, get married, become a mum or dad, learn to drive, become a grandma or a granddad – these age-associated events can be written up on a class chart.

Invite the children to find out more about the life cycle of a creature that has distinct phases in its life, for example, the frog.

Assessment

Note and collate all the children's individual contributions to the lessons, their drawings and written work.

Food

Learning targets

The children should know:

1 ➡→ about food likes and dislikes
2 ➡→ why we need food and drink
3 ➡→ what food and drink does for our bodies
4 ➡→ that animals eat and drink
5 ➡→ what some other animals eat

Before you start

Lesson preparation

Lesson 1

Collect food packaging and advertising as well as pictures of a variety of foods. Include as many fresh foods as possible as well as foods from a variety of cultures. Paper plates and drawing materials are also required. A sample food from each of the food groups would be useful in the nutrition discussion. There are some examples on Copymaster 11. Photocopy Copymaster 11.

Lesson 2

No special equipment is needed but you may wish to use a large sheet of 2 cm squared paper for the chart at the end of the lesson.

Lesson 3

Assemble a collection of pictures (these can be outline drawings) or models of a range of animals, drawings of foods that the animals might eat as shown on page 13, along with models or pictures of a horse trough, an animal drinking bowl, drinks containers for caged animals and a plastic cup. Obtain video footage of a range of animals eating. Photocopy Copymaster 12.

Investigations

Secondary sources about some of the foods we eat are required here.

Health and safety

Warn the children against eating wild fruits and berries. Remind them of the importance of washing their hands before preparing food, before eating food and after going to the lavatory.

Teaching the lessons

Lesson 1

Vocabulary

Beans, body, bread, butter, cereals, cheese, dislike, energy, fish, food, fruit, grow, health, juice, like, margarine, meat, milk, nuts, pasta, peas, potatoes, rice, vegetables; the names of foods the children talk about

Introduction `10min`

Using the food packaging material, advertisements and pictures, ask the children to tell you some foods they like and some they dislike.

Activities `25min`

Give each child a paper plate. Ask them to draw foods they like and stick them on the plate.

Bring the class together to look at some of the children's plates of food. Ask the children why we need food. Write their answers on the board.

Hand each child a copy of **Copymaster 11** and quiz the children as a class about which foods are body building, which ones give us energy and which ones keep us healthy (corresponding to the protein foods, the starchy foods and those containing vitamins and minerals). Copymaster 11 will be needed again for homework at the end of the lessons.

Closing the lesson `10min`

With quick-fire questioning ask individual children to name a food on Copymaster 11, for example:

Name a high-energy food. (Cereals, pasta, potatoes, bread, rice.)

What do meat and fish do in our bodies? (Build them.)

Name a body-building food. (Beans, cheese, fish, meat, nuts, peas.)

Which foods supply things called vitamins and minerals that keep us healthy? (Fruit, fruit juice, vegetables.)

Lesson 2 ② ③

Vocabulary

Dehydrated, drink, fluid, water and the names of the drinks the children have

Introduction — 10min

Ask the children to name all the drinks they have. List them on the board.

Activities — 30min

Invite the children, working in groups, to collect from each member of their group, the following data:

How many drinks do you have in a day?

What are the names of those drinks?

They can produce a tally for each child, which may, for example, say this:

Name: Terry **Number of drinks**: 6

Water	*Tea*	*Fizzy drinks*	*Squash*	*Pure juice*
2	1	1	0	2

Bring the class together and discuss and compare the information from the different groups. Decide how it is to be collated. Help the children to make a giant tally chart, pictogram or block graph.

Closing the lesson — 5min

Ask the children why it is that we need to have drinks and confirm that they understand that our bodies are mostly made of fluid (including a lot of water) which we need to replace continually to stay healthy. If we allow thirst to continue, our bodies become dehydrated.

Lesson 3 ④ ⑤

Vocabulary

Bottle, bowl, eat, drink, food, trough, water; names for the animals used in the lesson, along with the names of the foods they eat

Introduction — 5min

Review the kinds of foods that humans eat and point out that we eat all kinds of things, including cereal foods, fruit, meat and vegetables. Ask the children what cows, sheep and other farm animals eat. Then ask what some wild meat-eating creatures eat.

Activities — 30min

Ask the children to go round the room and match the animals to what they eat. They can collate the information using **Copymaster 12** as a record sheet.

Using models or pictures of a horse trough, an animal drinking-bowl, drinks containers for caged animals and a plastic cup, remind the children that animals need to drink water just as we do. Allow them to watch the video and ask them to spot the animals eating and drinking. It can be stopped from time to time to point out what the animals are eating or how they are drinking.

Closing the lesson — 5min

Go round the room giving the children the answers to the animal food quiz.

After the lessons

Homework

Give each child a copy of Copymaster 11. Ask them, over three days, to tick each of the foods every time they have a helping. The copymasters can be brought back to school for a follow-up discussion.

Investigations

Ask the children to compile a picture puzzle, for example, a join-up game or maze, which allows them to connect animals to the foods they eat. These can be printed for other children to play the games.

Choose a food, for example, banana, and ask the children to find out all they can about that food. Collate their information at the end of the day.
A study of bananas might yield the following facts: banana is a fruit, bananas help to keep us healthy, bananas come from palm trees, bananas grow in hot countries, some animals such as chimps, for example, eat bananas, bananas are used to make other foods such as banana split and are eaten with other foods such as breakfast cereal.

Assessment

To assess the children, consider asking the class to make a presentation to other classes on which you can make assessment observations. View their written work and their participation in the lessons.

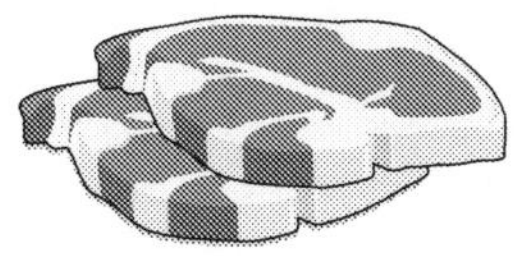
meat

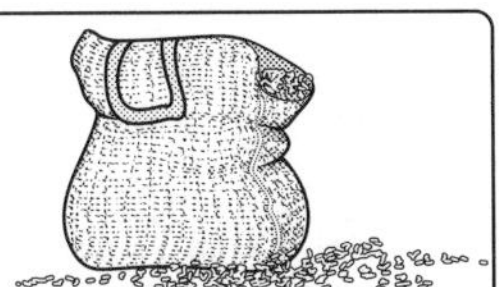
grain and seeds

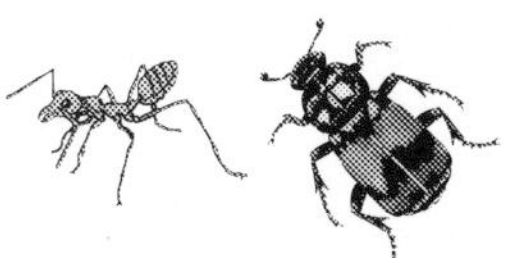
insects

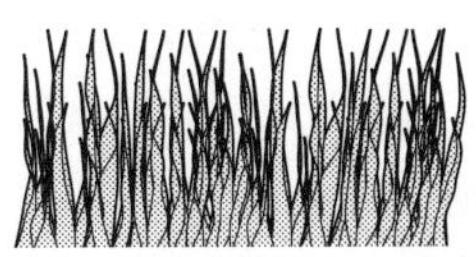
grass

Being ill, getting better

Learning targets

The children should know:

1 ➡➤ what we mean by illness
2 ➡➤ what we do to care for people who are ill
3 ➡➤ what medicines are
4 ➡➤ about medicines and safety
5 ➡➤ some things the body does to combat illness

Before you start

Lesson preparation

Lesson 1

If there is a camp bed available in a home corner, set up the corner like a hospital room. Alternatively, use the school's medical room if there is one. If neither of these is possible, borrow a doll's bed or cot, doll and bedding. Photocopy Copymaster 13.

Lesson 2

A visitor with a medical background is essential for this lesson. Perhaps the school nurse, the district nurse or a parent who is a doctor or a nurse could be invited into the classroom. Ask them to bring along a first-aid kit, a medical bag and any equipment they think appropriate. Before the lesson, begin the setting up of a classroom display, as shown on page 25. The drawings the children do in the lesson can be added to the display and used in the final discussion.

Lesson 3

Contact the local health centre to get hold of leaflets about medicines and safety. Borrow the school first-aid kit for the lesson. Photocopy Copymaster 14.

Investigations

The children may find that clipboards are useful.

Health and safety

There are very important health and safety issues to be discussed with the children in this lesson and as a result of the homework. In the lessons themselves, the children will not be at risk.

There may be children in the class or the school who have medical conditions of which other children are aware. If this is the case, talk to the parents of these children about the work being done in school so that the children's conditions can be sympathetically mentioned if this is appropriate. Be certain to get the facts right and avoid reinforcing misinformation about the conditions.

Teaching the lessons

Lesson 1 ① ②

Vocabulary

Get better, ill, illness, medicine, rest, sleep, well; other words raised in the discussion

Introduction   10 min

▨ Ask the children what we mean by illness and gather their ideas together. Persuade them to say how they felt when they were ill. List for the children some aspects of illness, including, for example, feeling hot or cold due to running a temperature, not feeling hungry due to loss of appetite, and some symptoms like spots, aches and pains.

Activities   25 min

▨ Using the home corner with the camp bed or the medical room, invite a child to act as the person not feeling well. Put the child to bed and discuss with the children what things we do for people who are ill. If you do not have access to a full-sized bed, carry out the actions with a doll in a play bed. List the recommendations the children suggest along with the following:

Put the person to bed to rest the body.

Cover them with a blanket to keep them warm.

Give them food that is easy to digest.

Give them plenty to drink.

Keep noise and light levels low to allow rest.

Give them appropriate medicine.

👤 Invite the children to complete **Copymaster 13** and include the sort of things discussed in the previous activity.

Closing the lesson   5 min

▨ Review with the children some of the ways that we feel when we are ill and how we care for people who are ill.

Lesson 2

Vocabulary

Bottle, box, linctus, medicine, pills, tablets; other words for equipment or actions described by the visitor; vocabulary of recovery used by the visitor – the latter may include words like blood, bugs, cure, disease, germs, signs, 'soldiers', symptoms

Introduction [5 min]

Introduce the visitor to the children.

Activities [35 min]

Invite the visitor to talk to the children about medicines, describing what they are and how they help our bodies to recover from illness. Make certain that the children are aware of the fact that medicines are powerful drugs that are given to specific individuals for specific illnesses and that no medicine, especially those prescribed by a doctor, must be taken by anyone else under any circumstances.

Divide the class into groups and ask each group to compile a picture to show one of the points the visitor made in their talk. Help each group to choose a different topic.

Closing the lesson [10 min]

Add some of the children's drawings to the class display. Below is a sample display.

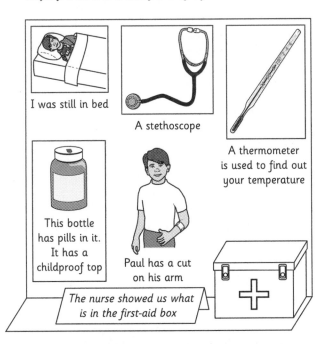

I was still in bed

A stethoscope

A thermometer is used to find out your temperature

This bottle has pills in it. It has a childproof top

Paul has a cut on his arm

The nurse showed us what is in the first-aid box

Lesson 3 ⑤

Vocabulary

Corrosive, danger, harmful, irritant, medicine, safe, safety, toxic; everyday explanations of these words

Introduction [10 min]

Using the display set up in Lesson 2 and the safety points made by the visitor in that lesson, begin to talk to the children about their own safety regarding

medicines. Encourage the children to contribute to a list of 'don'ts'. This list could include the following:

Never touch medicine bottles or tablets.

Never taste or smell things without checking with an adult first.

Do not try childproof caps, they are there to prevent the containers being opened.

Never take medicines intended for someone else.

Never go to a medicine cabinet or first-aid box without the help of an adult.

Draw a white cross on a green background and point out that this is the sign put on first-aid boxes.

Activities [20 min]

Tell the children that medicines are not the only substances we need to be wary of. Explain that there are liquids, powders and even tablets (for example, dishwasher tablets) that are used for cleaning and in the garden, all of which can be dangerous if they are tasted or smelled or if they get on the skin. Draw on the board each of the signs that appear on **Copymaster 14** and ask the children what they think each one means. Explain what each sign means using not only everyday words but also the words that appear on the bottom half of Copymaster 14. Point out that warning signs are often triangles but on bottles of cleaning fluids, for example, the same sign may appear in a square. All the signs are yellow and black.

Give each child a copy of Copymaster 14. Invite them to colour all the signs yellow. They can then talk to a classmate about what the signs mean. If there is time, they can cut the signs out, and stick one copy of each down the left-hand side of a piece of paper. They can then write in where they have seen or might see each of the signs.

Closing the lesson [10 min]

Reiterate the main points of the lesson, checking that all the children understand the dangers of medicines and other substances.

After the lessons

Homework

Allow each child to take home a copy of Copymaster 14. They should fold back the bottom half, then ask some of the people in their household what each of the signs mean. They can report back to school on whether their family knew about these signs.

Investigations

Investigate the occurrence of hay fever in the class, the likely causes, how people feel when they have hay fever and what medicines they take.

Ask the children to find out from an older child or an adult in school how it feels and how they were treated when they (a) fell over and cut themselves, (b) had a cold.

Assessment

Note the degree to which the children participate in the discussion. This topic is a good test of listening skills and of the children's general knowledge about health and safety.

Pets

Learning targets

The children should be able to:

1 ➡→ name some pet animals
2 ➡→ collect and collate data about pet ownership
3 ➡→ explain the diets and care of some pets
4 ➡→ identify which pets exhibit a range of behaviours

Before you start

Lesson preparation

Lesson 1

If appropriate, collect data about pet ownership from other classes in the school. It could take the form of counts; for example, how many people in a particular class have a dog or cat. Photocopy Copymaster 15.

Lesson 2

Create an animal-care display in the classroom. An example display is shown on page 27. Invite a professional who works with animals, such as a veterinary nurse, a police-dog handler or an RSPCA inspector to talk to the children.

Lesson 3

Look for some video footage of pet animals. Photocopy Copymaster 16.

Investigations

Build up a classroom resource box about pets. Include books, posters and CD-ROMs. Collect together some containers and labels for pet food, including full cans, can labels, and full and empty dry-food boxes and seed bags.

Health and safety

Follow LEA/school guidelines if live animals are brought near the children. Children should wash their hands after handling any animal. Be aware that some children may have an allergic reaction to animal fur and feathers.

Teaching the lessons

Lesson 1

Vocabulary

Names of common pets, including bird, cat, dog, fish, guinea pig, hamster, rabbit; words the children use; it may be important to explain such words as collection, data, record, tally

Introduction ⌞10min⌟

▦ Ask the children to name some kinds of pet. Compile a list with their help. Allow some individuals to tell the rest of the class about their pet.

Activities ⌞25min⌟

👥 Divide the class into pairs, give each child a copy of **Copymaster 15** and a list of the first names of all the children in the class. Allow the children time to ask everyone in the class which pet they have listed on Copymaster 15. They should tick or cross off the name of each person who answers their questions.

▦ Go through the replies recorded on the copymasters, compiling a master tally sheet. Note that some children have more than one kind of pet, so the total should exceed the number of children in the class.

Closing the lesson ⌞15min⌟

▦ If data is available from other classes in the school this can be compared with that collected by the class. A 'Top Pet' can be named and the children can be asked questions that require interpretation of the data. Here are some sample questions.

How many people in the class have a guinea pig?

How many people in the class have a pet that cannot fly?

Which pet is the least popular in the class?

Which pet is the most popular in the school? Why do you think that is?

How many goldfish owners are there in the school?

Lesson 2

Vocabulary

Care, diet, groom, health check, look after; names of pet foods; other words the children use

Introduction ⌞10min⌟

▦ Invite individual children to talk to the class about how they look after their pet. If you have a visiting expert, introduce them to the class.

Activities `25min`

 Either allow the visiting expert to talk about the care of animals or create a large class chart with headings as shown here.

	Dog	**Cat**	**Bird**	**Rabbit**	**...**
Diet	Dog food Meat Bones Biscuit				
Care	Warmth Place to sleep Brush and bath Exercise				

Allow the children time to record something they learned from the visitor or to make their own copy of part of the class chart. This record can be pictorial or written.

Closing the lesson `10min`

Draw the children's attention to the classroom display to emphasize some of the points made in the lesson. Here is an example of a display:

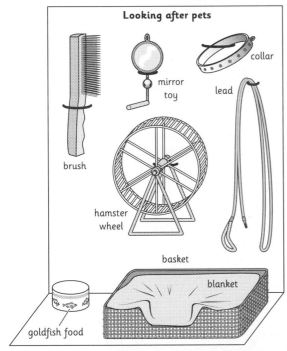

Looking after pets

brush, mirror, toy, collar, lead, hamster wheel, basket, blanket, goldfish food

Lesson 3 ④

Vocabulary

Names of pets, including bird, cat, dog, fish, guinea pig, hamster, rabbit; attributes/behaviours of all animals and of some species, for example, bark, breathe, chase, chew, eat, excrete, drink, fly, groom, grow, have babies, hop, jump, live in the air, live underwater, move, peck, roll over, scratch, see, swim; other words used by the children

Introduction `10min`

Explain to the children that this lesson is about the behaviour of animals. Hold up in turn pictures of each of a number of pets and ask the children to name some of the things these creatures do.

Activities `30min`

Watch some video footage of pets with the children, stopping the video to point out some of the things that all creatures do and the behaviour that is specific to particular species.

Ask the children to talk about **Copymaster 16** in pairs.

Closing the lesson `5min`

Highlight for the children the characteristics of all animals, using the words listed on Copymaster 16.

After the lessons

Homework

Ask those children who have a pet to make a picture to show what the creature does during one day. Those children who do not have a pet of their own could study a pet belonging to a relative. Here are some suggestions for recording the information.

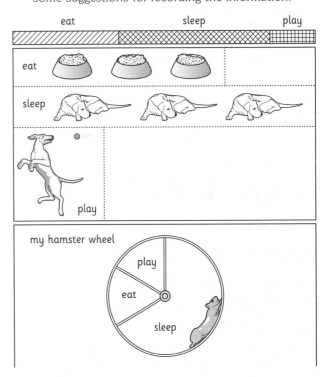

my hamster wheel

Investigations

Ask the children to find someone in school who keeps an unusual pet and talk to them about it, then report back to the class.

Invite the children to gather some wrappings for pet food and look at what the foods have in them, then make a little book describing the eating habits of a range of pets.

Assessment

According to each child's own life experiences, some of the class will be extremely knowledgeable about pets, while others may never have had a pet. Some children may, therefore, need further contact with or visits to see animals. There are valuable opportunities to check how all the children are handling scientific data in this topic.

Mini-beasts

Learning targets

The children should be able to:

1 ➡➤ help to find and collect small creatures
2 ➡➤ say that small creatures are alive
3 ➡➤ say that these animals need care like all other living things
4 ➡➤ understand that these creatures are animals
5 ➡➤ describe and draw mini-beasts
6 ➡➤ understand where mini-beasts live

Before you start

Lesson preparation

Lesson 1

Access to an outside location where there are likely habitats for small creatures is essential. Some creatures need collection for observation back in the classroom. Thus extra adult help would be invaluable. Collecting boxes would be useful. Photocopy Copymaster 17.

Lesson 2

Magnifiers would be useful for all the children in this lesson. Photocopy Copymaster 18.

Lesson 3

Enough large pebbles to give one to each work group in the class will be needed. Scissors for all the children are also necessary.

Investigations

CD-ROMs with pictures of mini-beasts on them, suitable protective clothing, samples of leaf litter, junk modelling materials, scissors and glue are all needed for the investigations.

Health and safety

Children need to wash their hands after handling soil, stones and leaves. Small creatures need care to preserve their lives. They should be collected in appropriate containers by adults, kept out of extremes of temperature, extremely dry conditions and direct sunlight, and returned to the spot where they were collected as soon as possible after the lessons.

Teaching the lessons

Lesson 1 ①②③

Vocabulary

Hidden, leaves, mini-beasts, soil, stones; words the children use when outside searching for small creatures

Introduction [5min]

▦ Begin the lesson by explaining that the children are going to help search for small creatures outside in the garden. Make it clear to the children that the creatures are alive and need care. They should not pick them up but should ask an adult to try collecting the creature for them.

Activities [25min]

▦ When outside, ask the children at which sites they might find small creatures. Allow the children to watch while you inspect the sites they choose. Show them how to collect about half a dozen small creatures in see-through specimen boxes. Return to the classroom with the collected creatures and the children.

👤 Give each child a copy of **Copymaster 17** and invite them to record what they did outside in a picture story.

Closing the lesson [5min]

▦ Review with the children what they have done and confirm that these small creatures are alive and need care.

Lesson 2 ④⑤

Vocabulary

Draw, move, name, observe, record; words the children use in describing the creatures

Introduction [5min]

▦ Remind the children that the live creatures collected require care and that the children may look at them but not touch them and should disturb them as little as possible.

Activities `30min`

Divide the class into groups. Allow each group to have one creature in a container. They can look through the container and make a drawing of the creature. These can be swapped round once the children have completed a drawing so that they can draw other creatures.

Ask the children to pair up. Give each child a copy of **Copymaster 18**. Read the names aloud to the children, then let them talk about which creatures they have drawn or seen when outside.

Closing the lesson `10min`

Ask the children to name some of the features of living things. Confirm with them that these small creatures have these features (for example, they eat, move, sense, have babies) and that they are animals. Tell the children that the living creatures removed from the garden for study have to be returned to the same spot they came from so that they can go on with their lives there.

Lesson 3 ⑥

Vocabulary

Creature, damp, habitat, leaf litter, live, rotting wood, stones; words the children use in connection with the sites where the creatures studied were found

Introduction `10min`

Ask the children to describe where the small creatures were found. Then ask them what the living conditions were like for the creatures. Tease out the fact that many of these creatures like cool, damp, dark conditions, where there is vegetation, some of which may be rotting.

Activities `30min`

Divide the class into groups and give each group a large stone, some drawing materials and scissors. Using their own observations and pictures from books, the children can draw some creatures which can be cut out and placed round and partly under the stone.

Create a class display of the children's work as shown below.

Closing the lesson `5min`

Remind the children of where small creatures are likely to be found. Introduce them to the word 'habitat' to describe such a location.

After the lessons

Homework

Ask the children to find and observe a spider in their home or garden. They can draw it, then write some things they observe about it. For example, they can compare it in size to something else that is very small (for example, a button), comment on its colour, whether it is shiny, smooth or hairy and how it behaves when disturbed.

Investigations

Allow the children to access CD-ROMs and look for pictures and video sequences about mini-beasts.

Ask the children to examine some leaf litter for small creatures while under adult supervision and while wearing protective clothing.

Invite the children to create an enormous replica of a mini-beast, giving it the correct external features.

Assessment

Note the children's observational skills and their attention to detail in their drawings.

Who lives here?
This is a habitat for many small animals

large stones

fallen leaves

damp ground

29

Get moving!

Learning targets

The children should know:

1 ➤➤ why we need exercise
2 ➤➤ how we move
3 ➤➤ about movement in other animals

Before you start

Lesson preparation

Lesson 1

Access to the hall or playground for a movement lesson is important here.

Lesson 2

A real or model skeleton would be useful for this lesson. There are also CD-ROMs available giving three-dimensional images for the children to look at. Photocopy Copymaster 19.

Lesson 3

Acquire some video footage of different animal movements. These should include the movements of fish or other aquatic creatures like seals or dolphins, reptiles like snakes, as well as birds and mammals. The children will also need books and other resources giving details of animal movement. Photocopy Copymaster 20.

Investigations

Access to resources about famous sports people and their injuries and access to adults around the school are required for these activities.

Teaching the lessons

Lesson 1 ①

Vocabulary

Active, body systems, breathing, exercise, fit, fitness, hot, perspire

Introduction ⌐5min⌐

▓ Ask the children for their own ideas about what we mean by exercise. Check that they know that keeping our bodies on the move helps our body systems work properly and helps to keep weight in check.

Activities ⌐30min⌐

▓ Allow the children a warm-up session with running on the spot and bends and stretches. Stop the children and ask them how they are feeling; for example, they may say that they are getting hot and breathing faster or that their heart is beating faster. Make a list of their responses.

▓ Invite the children to work with a partner to devise a sequence of, say, four movements, which they can repeat, to show some of the movements they can make.

▓ Discuss again with the children their ideas about what exercise is and its effect on the body.

Closing the lesson ⌐5min⌐

▓ Assure the children that we do not need to exercise until we are exhausted for the exercise to be good for us.

Lesson 2 ②

Vocabulary

Bones, move, movement, muscles, skeleton

Introduction ⌐5min⌐

▓ Ask the children what enables our bodies to move. Write on the board some of the words they use.

Activities ⌐30min⌐

▓ If there is a skeleton or model available, show this to the children. Though this is not a lesson about bones, the children should be interested to learn that we have a skeleton that forms a framework for our bodies, protects our soft insides and provides attachment points for the muscles. It is the muscles that enable the body to move.

▓ Give each child a copy of **Copymaster 19** and ask them to make a drawing of themselves on the move.

▓ Discuss with the children the kinds of movements we can make. Point out that we move on two limbs, our legs, unlike most other creatures, and that we can make very big movements and very small, careful ones like threading a bead on a necklace or colouring a picture.

Closing the lesson ⌐10min⌐

▓ Allow some children to mime a range of human movements in front of the class.

Lesson 3 ③

Vocabulary

Animals, move, movement; words describing kinds of movement such as gallop, run, slide, slither, trot

Introduction `5min`

Ask the children to give you some words that describe the ways in which animals move. Add these words to the class vocabulary list.

Activities `35min`

Watch some video footage of animals on the move, stopping or slowing the tape from time to time so that the children can view particular sequences in detail.

Divide the class into groups. Allow each group to choose a different animal, find out how it moves and draw pictures of it moving on **Copymaster 20**. Show the children examples of movement sequences as a model of what is required. Below is an example.

Closing the lesson `10min`

Review the set of lessons, reminding the children that we need exercise, that moving is made possible by muscles and that different creatures move around in different ways.

After the lessons

Homework

Ask the children to make an exercise diary for the people in their household for one week. For example, they can draw mum walking the dog and doing aerobics, dad walking to the station and the pet hamster in its exercise wheel.

Investigations

Ask the children to find out about sports injuries involving the muscles of footballers, runners and athletes.

Invite the children to find out which are the favourite sports and other exercise activities pursued by all the adults in school.

Assessment

Children's individual contributions to discussion and to practical work are the surest indicators of their learning here.

A caterpillar moves like this

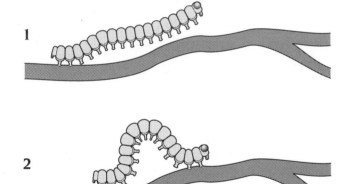
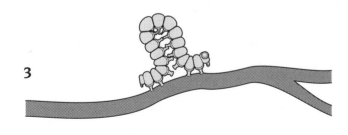
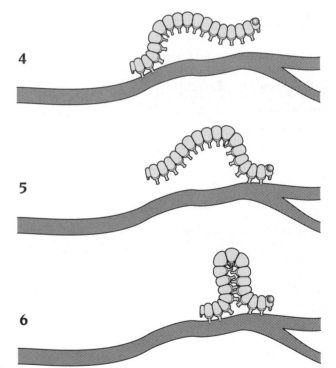

What is a plant?

Learning targets

The children should be able to:

1 ➤➤ name some plants
2 ➤➤ name some plants we eat
3 ➤➤ say that plants are alive
4 ➤➤ say why plants are important

Before you start

Lesson preparation

Lesson 1

Collect some books that enable you to identify plants. Prior to the lesson, walk round the school garden, or a local garden to which the children could be taken during the lesson, and note the plants growing there and their names. In the classroom, set up a display of fruits and vegetables that the children can inspect and handle. An example display is shown below. Photocopy Copymaster 21.

Lesson 2

Mount a class workshop around the room with some pot-grown plants. Each will require a card caption, explaining that plants drink, have babies, grow and need food. If the plants are set out as shown in the Lesson 2 Activities, the children will have clues about where they should draw each answer on Copymaster 22. The captions should be hidden until the children have completed the work on the copymaster which needs to be photocopied.

Lesson 3

Books and other resources giving information about creatures that are plant eaters are required.

Investigations

You will need Polaroids® of plants in the school garden to create a quiz and illustrated books about plants for the children to find the names of the plants. Obtain parental permission to take the children to a garden centre. In addition, collect resources that contain illustrations and information about the Venus flytrap, the pitcher plant and other carnivorous pants.

Health and safety

Remind the children that they should on no account pick, damage or destroy plants. Neither should they try tasting any part of a plant unless it has been given to them as food by an adult. The skin of some children is sensitive to some plants.

Teaching the lessons

Lesson 1   ① ②

Vocabulary

The names of the plants the children will see outside

Introduction |15min|

▓ Take the children outside to look at some growing plants. These can include wild and cultivated plants. Name the plants for them. Ask them to point to other examples of the same plant.

Activities |30min|

▓ Consolidate the work the children have done outside, giving them the names of some of the common plants around them.

▓ Ask the children to name the fruits and vegetables in the display. Then ask them to tell you which parts of the plants these are. Point out that some parts grow above ground while others grow below it. This will set the scene for the next topic, Plant labels.

Can you name these fruits and vegetables?

Which of these do you like to eat?

Give each child a copy of **Copymaster 21** and ask them to complete it, talking to a friend about what they have done.

Closing the lesson
5min

Hold up individual items from the display and ask individual children to name them.

Lesson 2 ③

Vocabulary

Words to explain essential processes for all living things, for example, drink, feed, grow, have babies, move; breathe, get rid of waste and sense may also be needed, though the children cannot be expected to detect these in the plants in the lesson

Introduction
10min

Point out to the children that they are expected to use the plants on display to show some of the things plants do that indicate that they are alive. Quiz the children about the characteristics of all living things. Here is an example of a display.

see-through bowl of water

| Why do we put plants in soil? | What will happen to the water you see in the bowl? |

| Can you see what this plant does? | What does this tell you about what plants do? |

Activities
20min

Allow the children to move about the room, drawing on **Copymaster 22** the plants on display to illustrate what plants do.

Closing the lesson
15min

Ask a volunteer to stand in front of the class and remind the others that the child eats, drinks, senses, moves and so on. Now place a plant next to the child and remind the children that the plant is also alive and that the characteristics of living things therefore apply to both the child and the plant.

Lesson 3 ④

Vocabulary

The names of some animals that eat plants

Introduction
10min

This lesson is to set the scene for later learning about food chains and the idea that plants are essential to the presence of animal life on Earth. Introduce the children to a range of plant-eating creatures. Include not only mammals but also examples from other animal groups including invertebrates.

Activities
25min

With the children watch a wildlife programme showing plant-eating animals.

Invite the children to draw pictures of grass and other plant material in the centre of a sheet of paper. They can then draw animal pictures round the edge of the paper and connect them up to the plants to record that they all eat plants.

Closing the lesson
10min

Point out to the children that plants are vital not only to the creatures mentioned in this lesson but also to all creatures; those that eat meat or a variety of foods, eat creatures that eat plants.

After the lessons

Homework

Ask the children to draw the plant foods found in a typical supermarket. Make a class frieze of the pictures.

Investigations

Create a plant quiz using Polaroids® of plants in the school garden. See if the children can name them or find their names in books.

Take the children to a garden centre or florist's shop to look at plant care and the kinds of plants found there.

Animals eat plants but there are also some varieties of plants that supplement their food intake by catching insects. Allow the children to inspect a Venus flytrap or pitcher plant and find out how they catch insects.

Assessment

Note the children's contributions to discussion and their involvement in class work.

Plant labels

Learning targets

The children should be able to:

1 ➤➤ point to different kinds of plants, including trees
2 ➤➤ point to and name the main parts of a plant
3 ➤➤ read and write the names for parts of a plant
4 ➤➤ draw a plant and label its parts

Before you start

Lesson preparation

Lesson 1

Arrange for the children to be accompanied into the school garden, a neighbouring garden or to a park or woodland. Collect two or three samples of plants that are weeds and can, therefore, be uprooted (for example, a dandelion); they should, if possible, have full roots, leaves, stems and flowers visible. Sometime before you plan to conduct this lesson, plant and grow some mung beans or cress, away from the classroom and following the directions on the packet, so that they are sprouting and showing leaves ready for this lesson.

Lesson 2

You will need class-sized flashcards with the following words on them: plant, root, stem, stalk, leaf, flower. Photocopy Copymaster 23.

Lesson 3

You will need four living plants growing in pots for the children to examine and draw. Before the lesson, mount each one on a piece of card, masking all parts of the plant except the part you wish the children to identify. Check that the children have the opportunity to identify roots, stems, leaves and flowers. Photocopy Copymaster 24.

Below are examples of masked plants.

Investigations

Both you and the children will need repeated access to the school garden to undertake a renovation scheme. This should be planned with the permission of the head teacher and governors so that sponsorship and other support can be sought. These things will probably need to be bought: garden tools (light enough for the children to use); fertilizer or compost to enrich the soil.

Donated plants and adult help would be invaluable.

For the second investigation the children will need secondary sources with colour pictures to look up flower names and colours.

A collection of leaves of different shapes should be made, either from the school grounds or from a local park (with permission), for the final investigation.

Health and safety

The skin of some children is sensitive to some plants. Be wary of allowing children to handle plants and soil freely. Make sure that they do not put their hands near their mouths and that they wash their hands thoroughly after the lesson.

leaf

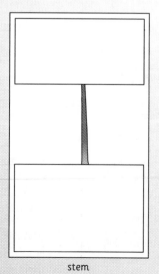
stem

root

Teaching the lessons

Lesson 1 ① ②

Vocabulary

Bush, flower, leaf, root, shrub, shoot, stem, tree

Introduction `15min`

In an outside setting, build on the children's knowledge of plants and point out to them that plants come in all shapes and sizes. Indicate that trees, bushes, hedges and grasses are all plants.

Activities `25min`

Within a selected outside area, make a whole-class tally of the numbers of trees, bushes/shrubs and plants bearing flowers. This can be recorded on a class flip chart.

Back in the classroom, show the class the uprooted plant and identify for the children the root, the stem, the leaf and the flower by pointing to these on the plant; then let several children in turn point them out.

Closing the lesson `5min`

Show the children some mung beans or cress that has been grown in appropriate conditions for this lesson. Point out to the children the root and the shoot or stem and the leaves.

Lesson 2 ③

Vocabulary

Flower, leaf, root, stem

Introduction `10min`

Show the children each of the class-sized flashcards in turn. Repeatedly hold them up, then ask individual children to call out what is on them.

Activities `30min`

Ask the children to pair up and give each child a copy of **Copymaster 23** and a pair of scissors. Invite them to cut along the lines on the copymaster to make a set of flashcards and a jigsaw of the plant picture. They should then play the following games with their partner.

Place one set of pieces face up in a jumble. Each child takes turns to make the plant picture and set the labels next to the appropriate parts of the picture.

Place both sets of pieces in two piles. Each child takes a pile and completes the picture and labelling, trying to be quicker than their partner.

Using the word cards only, turn both sets face down and jumble them. Each child takes turns to turn them up and find a matching pair. If a pair does not match, they turn the pair face down again. If the pair matches, they read out the word on the pieces and take that pair out of play. The object is to see who can collect more pairs.

Using the set of word and jigsaw flashcards from the above activity, the children can copy the words into their books or on to paper.

Closing the lesson `10min`

Hold up individual flashcards and ask the class to call out what they say.

Lesson 3 ③ ④

Vocabulary

Flowers, leaves, roots, stems

Introduction `10min`

Remind the children of the names of the parts of a plant.

Activities `30min`

Ask the children to examine and draw in detail one of the plants in the classroom.

Ask the children to go round the room in pairs, each child taking with them a copy of **Copymaster 24**. They should examine the numbered plants, in any order, draw the part of the plant they can see and record what it is called.

Closing the lesson `5min`

Bring the children together and check with the whole class the answers they should have on the copymaster.

After the lessons

Homework

Invite the children to grow cress seeds on a piece of moistened paper towel in a polystyrene food tray and bring it to school for a discussion session.

Investigations

Start a gardening club and encourage the children to help renovate the school garden.

Ask the children to find the names of three yellow flowers, three blue flowers and the names of flowers with colours besides these.

Invite the children to compare the shape and size of leaves from different plants, draw round the leaves and display them.

Assessment

Their contributions to whole-class activities, participation in the games and recording both in drawing and writing are important factors in making your judgements about the children's learning in this topic.

Let's grow

Learning targets

The children should be able to:

1 ➤➤ understand that plants have needs

2 ➤➤ confirm that plants need water

3 ➤➤ confirm that plants need light

4 ➤➤ say that plants need warmth

5 ➤➤ say that plants vary in the amount of light, water and warmth they require

Before you start

Lesson preparation

Lesson 1

Two similar plants in flowerpots are required. The seedlings of many plants are appropriate for this lesson, including beans and tomatoes. A small watering can would be useful. A house plant should be placed on display as shown on page 37. Photocopy Copymaster 25.

Lesson 2

Two weeks before taking this lesson, put two similar seedlings in pots in a growing medium and place one in good light (not direct sunlight) and the other in total darkness. Water them regularly. For the lesson, put them side by side.

Lesson 3

Posters and pictures showing the seasons, along with the house plants used in Lesson 1 are needed. Photographs of plants growing in shady conditions and in direct sunlight are also needed. Photocopy Copymaster 26.

Investigations

Two packets of runner bean seeds, jam jars, blotting paper or absorbent kitchen cloth, sunflower seeds, garden tools and access to washing facilities are important resources for these investigations.

Health and safety

As with all the plant topics, be aware of skin allergies and the dangers of smelling, tasting and handling plants as well as the need to care for the plants themselves. The children need reminding that when they have handled plants or soil, they should on no account put their hands near their mouths and should wash their hands thoroughly.

Teaching the lessons

Lesson 1   ① ②

Vocabulary

Grow, need, plant, thrive, water; words the children use during the lesson

Introduction   10 min

▓ Show the children the house plant on display and ask them what they think the plant needs. This plant will be useful again in Lesson 3.

Activities   30 min

▓ Take the two similar plants in flowerpots and explain to the children that you want to find out whether the plants need water to live. Ask the children how they think this could be done. Ask other children to evaluate the suggestions made. Point out that the plants will be placed in the same location but only one will be watered.

👤 Invite the children to write or draw how the experiment was set up, then record on **Copymaster 25** what they think will happen to the plants.

Closing the lesson   5 min

▓ Remind the children that the experiment needs daily review and that they should see if their predictions are confirmed in about a week or two.

Lesson 2   ③

Vocabulary

Light, needs, plant

Introduction   10 min

▓ Remind the children of the experiment set up in the previous lesson. Then tell them about the experiment set up at least two weeks earlier. Ask the children to predict what might have happened.

Activities

[20min]

▓ Produce the plants and ask for the children's comments. They should note that the plant kept in the dark may have lost the greenness of the leaves, and may look less robust and be thriving less well than the plant kept in the light.

👤 Ask the children to make a drawing of the results of this experiment, colouring the leaves appropriately, and write up what they have learned from it.

Closing the lesson

[10min]

▓ Hold up for the children to see some of the work they have done in the lesson. Compare again the plants kept in the different growing conditions.

Lesson 3 ④ ⑤

Vocabulary

Autumn, cold, grow, growth, hot, light, seasons, shade, soil, spring, summer, sun, water, winter

Introduction

[10min]

▓ Draw attention to the plant on display, to which flashcards should be added so that they indicate the plant's needs that the children now know about. The display may now look something like this:

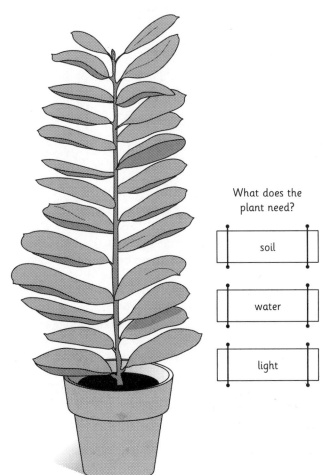

What does the plant need?

soil

water

light

This is a rubber plant
It is alive

Activities

[35min]

▓ Using the posters and other resources available, draw the children's attention to the fact that plants tend to grow more in the spring and summer. Ask the children why they think that is. Point out the weather differences in the seasons and confirm that one of the reasons for greater growth in spring and summer is that the warmth of these seasons promotes growth.

👤 Give each child a copy of **Copymaster 26** to complete. When they have done the colouring in, they can cut out the appropriate images and stick them onto a blank sheet of paper, to compile their own 'plant needs' chart.

▓ Though warmth does help plants grow, individual plants thrive in different conditions. Using photographs, the children's experience of plants in their own gardens and in the school gardens as well as other resources, discuss the fact that some plants like the full sun, others the shade and some grow on cool mountain tops, while others grow near warm beaches.

Closing the lesson

[10min]

▓ Use the flashcards from the display and hold them up one at a time, asking individual children to call out the needs of plants.

After the lessons

Homework

Ask the children to make some drawings or paintings of plants. They can see how many different ones they can draw.

Investigations

Give the children soaked runner bean seeds, jam jars and blotting paper and invite them to plant them and watch them grow.

Plant sunflower seeds in the school garden and monitor their growth with the children's help.

Assessment

There are some straightforward learning points in lessons on plant needs but these topics may raise plant consciousness for some children for whom plants are not an important feature in their everyday lives.

The extent to which they have listened and participated and the quality of their recording should all give assessment opportunities.

Plant babies

Learning targets

The children should be able to:

1 ➡➔ say that plants have babies
2 ➡➔ say that seeds form new plants
3 ➡➔ say that seeds are mostly found inside fruits
4 ➡➔ draw fruits and seeds and say from which plants they come

Before you start

Lesson preparation

Lesson 1

Make a collection of growing mature plants and their seedlings and also plants that put out runners, like the strawberry. The runners can then be seen attached to the parent plant. Small seed trays or plastic flowerpots and a soil-free growing medium, along with newspaper and access to washing facilities are important in this lesson. Painting and drawing equipment will be required. A cutting board and a knife may be needed.

Lesson 2

Collect a range of fruits and seeds for this lesson, including, for example, tomatoes, strawberries, plums, peas in the pod, non-edible seeds such as sycamore seeds and acorns, and seed heads from flowering plants. This kind of collection can be difficult to assemble in the same season of the year, though supermarket fruit counters do stock imported fruits at all times of the year which may help in the planning of this lesson. A board on which to cut open the fruits and a table knife are required. Photocopy Copymaster 27.

Lesson 3

If it is possible, assemble seeds from trees and seeds belonging to other plants which can be set alongside young plants and mature plants of the same species. Perhaps this can be done with some trees and plants in the school garden, in a neighbouring garden or at a garden centre. Find time-lapse video footage showing plant growth from seed to mature plant. Such footage is also available on some CD-ROMs. Photocopy Copymaster 28.

Investigations

An array of fruits and seeds, along with reference books and pictures of these fruits and the plants into which they grow are needed.

Health and safety

As with all the plant topics, be aware of skin allergies and the dangers of smelling, tasting and handling plants as well as the need to care for the plants themselves. The children need reminding that when they have handled plants or soil, they should on no account put their hands near their mouths and should wash their hands thoroughly.

Teaching the lessons

Lesson 1   ① ②

Vocabulary

Full grown, grow on, seed, seedling, transplant, young plant

Introduction   5min

▓ Introduce the children to the vocabulary for this lesson, checking whether anyone in the class can tell the other children what a seed and a seedling are.

Activities   35min

▓ Look carefully with the children at the growing mature plants and their seedlings, as well as plants that put out runners. Point out to the children that the seedlings are the young or 'babies' of the mature plant. Allow the children to observe the seed cases at the bottom of the shoots, if these are visible, and to determine whether the first leaves on the seedling look like those on the parent plants.

▓ Invite the children to paint or draw the young and mature plants which they have observed. This will form the children's record of their work.

▓ Spread out newspaper and allow the children to plant carefully some seedlings. They should all wash their hands thoroughly afterwards.

Closing the lesson   5min

▓ Bring the children together, hold up some of their drawings and remind them of the new vocabulary they have met in the lesson. Check that they understand that plants have young and that these seedlings will grow into plants like the parent plant.

Lesson 2 ③

Vocabulary

Flesh, fruit, pip, pit, seed, seed case, soft, stone; the names of the fruits used in the lesson

Introduction [5 min]

Hold up in turn each of the fruits and seeds collected and ask the children what it is and which plant it comes from. Tell them the names they do not know. Put the fruits and seeds into three groups. These groupings are based on appearance: firstly, those that are soft throughout such as gooseberries, strawberries and tomatoes; secondly, those that have a large stone such as peaches and plums; and thirdly, flower seed-heads, nuts in their cases and non-edible seeds such as ash-keys.

Activities [15 min]

Using the board, cut open some of the fleshy fruits, then the stone-bearing fruits and finally those that are flower seed heads, nuts and non-edible seeds. If several examples are cut open, they can be handed around for the children to look at.

Divide the class into groups and give each group examples of the cut-open fruits to look at and draw, using **Copymaster 27** if this is appropriate.

Closing the lesson [5 min]

Remind the children that the fruit of a plant commonly contains the seed and check that they understand that the seed will, under the right conditions, grow into a plant of the same kind.

Lesson 3 ④

Vocabulary

Grow, life cycle, phases, plant, seed, seeding; the names of the particular plants and fruits used in the lesson

Introduction [10 min]

Ask the children to tell you the sequence of the life cycle of a plant, starting with the seed. Invite a few volunteers to act out the growth of a seed into a mature plant, pretending that they themselves are the seed, then the root and the shoot and so on.

Activities [20 min]

View the seeds, seedling and plant chains in a chosen location.

Ask the children to draw pictures to record three of the phases of the life cycle of a plant on **Copymaster 28**.

Closing the lesson [15 min]

Show the children some time-lapse video footage of plant growth, stopping the film to show them the growth phases.

After the lessons

Homework

Invite the children to watch a gardening programme to see how seeds and seedlings are planted.

Invite the children to plant apple pips, orange pips, and avocado and peach stones in yoghurt pots and see whether they grow. They can be given an instruction sheet with the following or similar instructions.

Make some holes in the bottom of the pot so that the soil does not stay too wet.

Fill the pot with compost.

Carefully put the seed into the soil just below the surface.

Keep the pot in good growing conditions for several weeks.

Investigations

Give the children an array of fruits and seeds, along with reference books and pictures. Ask them to name as many as they can.

Give the children seeds they know about and ask them to find out about the mature plant and draw what it will look like.

Assessment

The children's enthusiasm for and participation in the activities will give clues to their learning, along with their responses to questions and work on the copymasters.

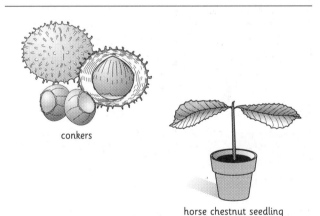

conkers

horse chestnut seedling

horse chestnut tree

Matching alike/unlike

Learning targets

The children should be able to:

1 ➡➤ spot similarities between animals
2 ➡➤ spot differences between animals
3 ➡➤ look at colours seen in animals and plants

Before you start

Lesson preparation

Lesson 1

Collect and display pictures and models of a wide range of animals. If you wish, these can all be of the larger vertebrates but small creatures can also be included. Those animals appearing on Copymaster 29 are all vertebrates and include examples of mammals, fish and birds. Leave the display for Lessons 2 and 3. Photocopy Copymaster 29.

Lesson 2

Arrange for the children to visit a farm, wildlife park, zoo, pet shop or private collection to see some live animals for this lesson. Extra adult help should be sought, not only for the trip but also for follow-up work. Use the display set up for Lesson 1.

Lesson 3

Add to the display set up for Lesson 1 to include pictures of brightly coloured animals. If possible, set up an equally arresting display of plants in flower. Photocopy Copymaster 30.

Investigations

Books, CD-ROMs and other resources for the young about camouflage will be needed.

Health and safety

In situations where children are in close proximity to animals, ask them to take care. Remember some children show allergic reactions to fur and feather.

Teaching the lessons

Lesson 1 ①

Vocabulary

The names of the animals on display, the names of the animals the children talk about, the names of features mentioned, for example, ears, horns, tails, wings

Introduction 15min

▦ Draw the children's attention to the display and allow them time to comment on and discuss the animals' features. For example, point to or hold up a picture and ask a child to describe the animal; point to a feature on an animal and ask what the children see. Emphasize that in this lesson they should look for things that are the same or similar about the animals.

Activities 20min

▦▦ Place the children into pairs and give each pair a copy of **Copymaster 29** and a pair of scissors. Ask them to cut along the lines on the copymaster so that they have a set of pictures which they can then talk about. They can take turns in putting together creatures that look similar; for example, creatures that have wings or tails.

▦▦ Form the pairs into groups and ask the children to each have a turn in putting together animals that are alike. Ask the children to see if each one in the group can find a different way of putting the pictures together.

Closing the lesson 10min

▦ Take up pairs of pictures or models from the display and ask the children how they are similar. See if they can tell you several ways in which some creatures are alike.

Lesson 2 ②

Vocabulary

The words required here will depend on where the children are taken and should include the names of animal and their features, such as feather, fur, hoof, horn

Introduction
[5min]

▓ As this is a lesson conducted during a visit away from the classroom, the children should already be in groups. Remind them that they are looking for differences between animals.

Activities
[30min]

◆◆ If this is a day trip, this activity can be done in a half-hour session during the day. Ask the children to look at the animals and make comparisons, noting especially the differences which they should record for discussion and follow-up in the classroom.

Draw their attention to the animals' features including the following: their shape and overall size, the sense organs such as ears, eyes and noses, their fur, hair, skin, feathers or scales, the hoofs, forelimbs and hind limbs, and the tail.

Closing the lesson
[10min]

▓ Draw the children together and remind them of what they have seen, emphasizing some of the differences between the animals.

Lesson 3   ③

Vocabulary

Camouflage, daisy, delphinium, hide, honeysuckle, peony, rose, scabious, see, snapdragon; the names of the animals on display; the vocabulary of colour

Introduction
[5min]

▓ To encourage the children to think about colour, hold up animal pictures and ask them what colour the creatures are.

Activities
[35min]

👥 Put the children into pairs and ask them to draw an animal of their choice and colour it as accurately as they can.

▓ Tell the children that some animals need to hide from other creatures that might kill and eat them. Explain that this is called camouflage and show some pictures of camouflaged animals. Point out that some predatory animals also use camouflage to conceal themselves from their prey. Explain that animals and flowers are sometimes highly coloured and easily seen for a purpose too. The animals may want to attract each other and the flowers need to attract bees and other insects.

▓ Examine **Copymaster 30** with the children, using the key shown right to name the plants. Show the children flowers from the display and talk about the colours of flowers.

👤 Invite the children to colour in Copymaster 30 to match the colour of the flowers.

Closing the lesson
[5min]

▓ The children should now be conscious that animals and flowers come in a wide range of colours. Their attention can be drawn back to the idea of camouflage.

After the lessons

Homework

Invite the children to draw two pictures of different animals side by side, or to cut out two animal pictures from a magazine. They can then connect and describe the similarities and differences. They could even do this with two of their own pets.

Investigations

Ask the children to choose an animal that uses camouflage. They could, for example, choose a moth, a stick insect, a snake, a chameleon or an animal like a tiger. They should find out all they can about it and draw a picture showing how well the camouflage works.

Invite the children to look at circumstances in which humans use camouflage and why (for example, in warfare and to get close to wildlife).

Assessment

Note the range of similarities and differences between animals that the children spot during the lessons and when observing real animals and plants.

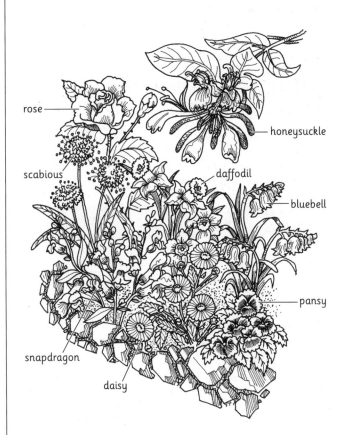

rose — honeysuckle — scabious — daffodil — bluebell — pansy — snapdragon — daisy

Looking at plants

Learning targets

The children should be able to:

1 ➠➤ say that flowers from different plants differ from one another
2 ➠➤ observe and draw leaves from different plants
3 ➠➤ make a miniature garden

Before you start

Lesson preparation

Lesson 1

Mount a display of flowers. These should include a range of different colours, shapes and sizes of flower. They can be cultivated, bought cut flowers or flowers from the school garden. Magnifiers will be useful for the children to view the flowers. A4 card for all the children, pre-folded three times to give a concertina shape is also necessary. Photocopy Copymaster 31. Out of school hours, walk round the immediate vicinity of the school and note down the locations of flowers which the children might see on their way to and from school.

Lesson 2

A collection of leaves are required for this lesson. A range of art materials will also be needed, including hard plastic sheet, paint rollers and paint, felt-tip pens, wax crayons, pencil crayons and chalk, masking tape, overalls and newspaper. Photocopy Copymaster 32. Extra adult help would be invaluable so that the children can do all the practical activities.

Lesson 3

Containers in which to make small gardens are required. Ice cream tubs are suitable. Also required are scissors or a skewer for making holes, polystyrene chips or shapes, a planting medium (for example, free-draining compost with 25 per cent grit or coarse sand), pebbles, gravel, small plants and a watering can of water. Daisies, grass and clover along with any rockery plants should thrive in these conditions.

Investigations

A flower press or old newspapers or blotting paper and heavy books are needed. Try to secure the opportunity for the children to collect leaves for themselves.

Health and safety

In all lessons where plants are present, take care of those children with sensitive skins, skin allergies and hay fever. Ensure that the children do not attempt to taste plant material and wash their hands thoroughly after handling plants. Take care not to include parts from any plant known to be poisonous, for example, foxglove.

Teaching the lessons

Lesson 1 ①

Vocabulary

The names of the flowers on display; words for describing flowers including those relating to colour, shape, size and location where flowers might grow; the seasons and months of the year when flowering might take place

Introduction [10min]

▦ Present the flower display to the children and talk to them all about the features of the flowers in it.

Activities [30min]

♣ Divide the class into groups and give each group one or two sample plants so that all the children can look closely at them. Magnifiers would be useful. Allow the children to talk in their groups. Afterwards, call the attention of all the class to each group in turn so that children from each group can describe their flowers.

▦ Give out copies of **Copymaster 31** and talk it through with the children, drawing attention to the flowers on the display.

👤 Ask each child to draw some example flowers. These can be from the display, specimens they have brought in (like daisies from the playing field) or flower pictures in botany books. If they draw them on the little concertina and add their names, as shown on page 43, the children will have a record of their experience of flowers with different features and be starting to name them.

42

this is a pansy · this is a bird of paradise · this is a sunflower · these are daisies

Closing the lesson   5 min

Talk about and name the flowers found in locations near the school so that the children can extend their learning of flowers to when they are out of school.

Lesson 2   2

Vocabulary

The names of the plants from which the leaves come; words the children use or need in describing leaf shapes

Introduction   10 min

Point out the collection of leaves and hold up several leaves in turn for the children to describe. Explain that the children will be making pictures with leaves so that they have plenty of opportunities to look at them very carefully.

Activities   30 min

Set up this and the following two activities so that each group of children has a chance to move round, swapping activities to allow everyone to have a turn. Show the children how to make leaf roller-prints. Run the roller over the ink or paint pad, then over a leaf set down on old newspaper. Lay the inked leaf on a clean surface, inked face uppermost. Place a sheet of paper on top of the leaf and rub carefully. The print should come out on the paper.

Tape down the leaves on to paper using masking or layout tape which can be easily removed. Ask the children, still in their groups, to draw round the leaves with pencil crayons or felt-tip pens and talk about the leaf shapes. Ask them to match their drawings to leaf shapes on **Copymaster 32**.

Still in their groups, ask the children to put lightweight paper over the leaves laid face up, then carefully rub with crayon or chalk over the paper to reveal a textured picture of the leaf.

Closing the lesson   5 min

Bring together all the children's experiences by holding up some of their pictures, asking individual children to describe the leaves.

Lesson 3   3

Vocabulary

Container, garden, gravel, growing medium, light, soil, plant, warmth, water

Introduction   10 min

Explain to the children that they are going to have the chance to make a little garden of their own. Review with the children what plants need to maintain life.

Activities   30 min

Make holes in the bottom of a container and ask the children why it is important to do this. Place in the bottom some polystyrene chips and check that the children understand that this is to help with drainage. Scoop in some planting medium until the container is half full. Set three different plants in the medium. Scoop in more of the medium and firm it up round the plants. Ask the children why this is necessary. Decorate the surface with pebbles and add gravel to deter slugs and snails. Place the container in a suitable location and water the plants.

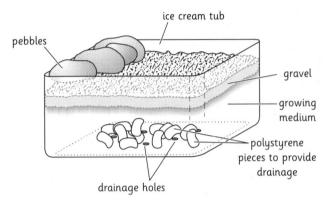

ice cream tub · pebbles · gravel · growing medium · polystyrene pieces to provide drainage · drainage holes

Ideally, every child should make their own garden but if resources do not permit this, they can make gardens in pairs. They should replicate what they saw you doing.

Closing the lesson   5 min

Review, with the children, how to make a miniature garden.

After the lessons

Homework

Allow the children to take home the gardens they made in school and continue to cultivate them, reporting back to the class about what they have done to maintain the growth of the plants.

Investigations

Invite the children to press leaves in a flower press or between sheets of newspaper or blotting paper and under heavy books. They can make a class scrapbook.

Invite the children to look out for plant records, for example, largest, smallest, most common.

Assessment

Devise a checklist related to, for example, flower features, leaf features and plant needs, and make an entry when you hear a child use these key words and phrases in the lessons.

Looking at animals

Learning targets

The children should be able to:

1 ➡️ recognize the sense organs in some animals

2 ➡️ compare animals according to size

3 ➡️ study one group of mammals, looking at differences between them

Before you start

Lesson preparation

Lesson 1

Resources containing pictures of animals, including books, posters, magazines (for example *National Geographic*) and CD-ROMs are needed. Access to live animals (for example, school pets) would be an advantage. Photocopy Copymaster 33.

Lesson 2

You will need similar resources to those for Lesson 1, along with animal size statistics. Animal record-breaker data and video footage may be a help and large sheets of card or paper. One wall of the classroom could be covered with paper in readiness for the lesson. Large felt-tip pens will be required. Adult help in drawing animal outlines of about the right size would be helpful.

Lesson 3

Choose a group of animals for class study, for example, big cats, bears or lizards. Get hold of as many pictures, books, posters and other resources as possible related to the chosen group. Set up display areas so that the whole study can be completed in the lesson. Photocopy Copymaster 34.

Investigations

The class collection of books about animals is important here.

Teaching the lessons

Lesson 1 ①

Vocabulary

Ape, bluebottle, buffalo, crocodile, ears, eyes, elephant, fox, grass snake, hearing, nose, perch, rabbit, sight, smell, taste, touch; the names of other animals referred to in the lesson

Introduction 10 min

▓ It is assumed that the children will have already done the work in Topic 3 Our senses. Ask the children what our senses are and review what they have already covered in Topic 3. Point out that all animals and plants sense what is happening round them.

Activities 30 min

▓ Look with the children at some of the resource material about animals and with each picture ask a volunteer to answer some challenges, such as, for example:

What is this animal? How does it hear?

(Pointing to the eyes.) What are these?

Whose ears can you see?

(Pointing to the nose.) What does this creature do with this?

 Give each child a copy of **Copymaster 33** and ask them to name the animals. The creatures are identifiable from their noses and ears. The eyes are those of a bluebottle, an ape, a perch and a grass snake.

▓ Review the work on the copymaster with the children, giving them the names of the creatures. Widen the discussion to include other animals with distinctive sense organs that help to identify them.

Closing the lesson 5 min

▓ Point out that if we look carefully at animals we can sometimes tell to which group of animals they belong.

Lesson 2 ②

Vocabulary

The vocabulary of size, including large, larger, largest, small, smaller, smallest, tall, taller, tallest, and measurements in centimetres and metres

Introduction
[10 min]

Choose a large animal like an elephant or wildebeest and, from information about its dimensions, create a life-sized outline. This can be done on sheets of newspaper stuck together. The shape can then be stuck on to the prepared display wall as shown here.

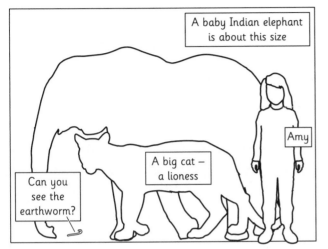

A baby Indian elephant is about this size

Amy

A big cat – a lioness

Can you see the earthworm?

Activities
[25 min]

Divide the class into groups and ask each group to find, with adult help, the size of another creature and cut out an outline from a different colour of paper. These can be attached to the board in front of the large outline.

Ask a child to lie on a sheet of paper and draw around them. Attach this outline to the display. Then choose a tiny creature like a woodlouse and cut one out of paper and attach that to the display.

Closing the lesson
[10 min]

Ask individual children to offer their comments on the display.

Lesson 3
(3)

Vocabulary

Words for and related to the group of animals chosen for study, for example, big cats: cheetah, claws, clean, ears, eyes, fur, hunt, jaguar, leopard, lion, moult, panther, paws, pounce, prey, prowl, sight, smell, sound, stalk, tail, tiger, whiskers

Introduction
[10 min]

Set the scene for the children's hour of work. Show the children the areas of the room that have been allocated to specific activities related to the chosen group of animals and explain what is expected of them in each one. Allow the children to follow the activities in a way which will enable everyone to finish. The children should work individually but it may prove more appropriate to get the children to work in groups. Here are some suggestions regarding room layout.

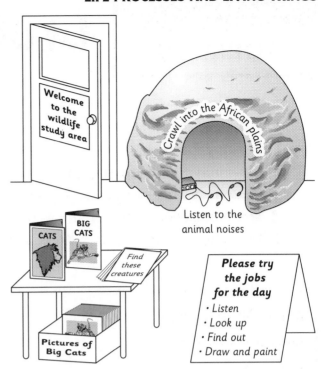

Welcome to the wildlife study area

Crawl into the African plains

Listen to the animal noises

CATS

BIG CATS

Find these creatures

Pictures of Big Cats

Please try the jobs for the day
· Listen
· Look up
· Find out
· Draw and paint

Activities
[30 min]

Allow each child to draw carefully a picture of one of the creatures chosen for study and discuss or name the parts of the animal.

Ask the children to try to make an entry under each of the headings on **Copymaster 34** about one of the creatures on display, spotting key features.

Invite the children to listen to taped animal calls, watch a video about the animals or do both.

Closing the lesson
[5 min]

Draw the children's attention to some of the key features of the animals chosen for study.

After the lessons

Homework

Ask each child to borrow a book about animals from the school library and use it to complete another copy of Copymaster 34.

Investigations

Invite each child to choose their favourite animal and find out what they can about it.

Set a quiz using the class books about animals. Photocopy pictures from the books and arrange them round the room with caption questions, such as, for example, 'Whose paws are these?', 'Which book has information about this animal?'. Such an investigation allows the children to practise using secondary sources.

Assessment

Consider the children's comments based on observations, the clarity of their recording and the concentration they show during the activities.

Grouping

Learning targets

The children should be able to:

1 ➤➤ name some mammals and know some of their characteristics
2 ➤➤ name some fish and know some of their characteristics
3 ➤➤ name some birds and know some of their characteristics

Before you start

Lesson preparation

Lesson 1

A mammal, for example, a cat or dog, would be invaluable for this lesson. If a live creature is not available, secondary sources will have to suffice. Assemble a collection of colour pictures of a wide range of animals, including those that may be familiar to the children and some that are not so common. Include aquatic mammals in the collection. Use books about mammals from the school or class library. Photocopy Copymaster 35.

Lesson 2

If the school has an aquarium with, for example, guppies or goldfish that the children can observe, this would be helpful. If there are no fish in your school, the children could be taken to a pet shop or garden centre where there are fish. There may also be a parent of one of the children who is willing to bring into school a single fish for the children to look at. Use books about fish from the school or class library. Photocopy Copymaster 36.

Lesson 3

The children need access to a location where they can look at birds. They could, for example, observe a school bird table or watch birds in the school garden. They could be taken to a bird park to see caged birds. Use books about birds from the school or class library.

Investigations

Secondary sources about mammals, fish and birds are required. For the second investigation, the children will need a live animal to watch over time.

Health and safety

As in all lessons where live creatures are present, take care that the children who have allergies are protected, that both children and animals are safe from harm and that, if the children handle the animals, they wash their hands afterwards.

Teaching the lessons

Lesson 1 ①

Vocabulary

Fur, hair, live babies, milk, teat; the names of the animals on view to the children; the names of other mammals they seek out in books and pictures.

Introduction [10min]

▦ Show the children the live creatures if available and pictures of mammals. Ask them to name these creatures. Tell them the names of those that are unfamiliar to them.

Activities [30min]

👤 Ask each child to draw pictures of some of the live creatures and of some of those in the secondary resources.

▦ Hold up the children's pictures and invite the children to compare different creatures.

▦ Give each child a copy of **Copymaster 35** and point out that all these creatures and all the others looked at in this lesson belong to a large group called mammals. Use the pictures to tease out some of the things that all these creatures have in common, namely that they have live babies and suckle their young, producing milk to do so. They are also warm-blooded but this fact cannot, of course, be gleaned from the pictures.

Closing the lesson [5min]

▦ Write up the word 'mammal' on the board and attach some of the animal pictures beneath it to emphasize that all these creatures are mammals.

Lesson 2 ②

Vocabulary

Bullhead, goldfish, guppy, stickleback, stone loach; the names of other fish available in classroom resources

Introduction | 10 min |

▓ Draw a fish outline on the board as shown here. Talk through some of its features, writing up clues for what the children should be looking for when they see real fish.

What do you see here? What are they for?

Where do fish live?

What does the fish use these for?

Activities | 30 min |

◆◆ Set up this and subsequent activities so that the children can take turns, in groups, doing them. Using the fish outline and clue questions that are on the board, the children should closely observe the real fish and draw pictures showing some of their features.

◆◆ Allow the children to look at the pictures of fish and read about fish in books.

◆◆ Give each child a copy of **Copymaster 36** and ask them to write in the boxes some of the things they have learned about fish.

Closing the lesson | 10 min |

▓ Review what the children have learned and spell out some of the characteristics of all fish, namely that they live in water, swim using fins and have gills. They are also cold-blooded but this will not be apparent from the pictures.

Lesson 3 ③

Vocabulary

The names of birds seen around the school or on the visit to a bird park

Introduction | 10 min |

▓ If the children go on a visit out of school, this lesson can be part of that day or take place before the visit. Introduce the lesson by finding out what the children know about birds and what they think distinguishes them from other creatures.

Activities | 25 min |

▓ Allow the children time to watch birds and to talk amongst themselves about their features and behaviour. Encourage the children to make comparisons based on features they can see.

▓ Ask the children to help you make a list of what they think the features of birds are. Check that the list includes the laying of eggs and having feathers. The children may also say that birds have wings and that birds fly. Birds are also warm-blooded but the children cannot be expected to know this merely from observing them.

Closing the lesson | 5 min |

▓ Draw the children's attention to the resources about birds by, for example, holding up pictures of birds and calling out their names, talking about the nesting materials that different birds use and how they care for their young.

After the lessons

Homework

The children can continue at home the investigation started in class by observing a family pet and recording what they discover. They can also list animals according to which group they belong and note which list is the longest.

Investigations

Invite the children to make a book of their own entitled 'My favourites'. They could choose some example mammals, fish or birds, or choose one of each, then draw pictures and write about them.

Allow the children time to make a detailed study of the behaviour of a live animal. For example, they could intently observe a goldfish for 10 minutes, recording when it swims, surfaces, feeds from the bottom, hides in the weed, and so on.

Assessment

The children will have had many opportunities to use their observational skills in this topic and assessments of these can be made. They should all, in addition, know some of the key features of mammals, fish and birds. A short picture or word test, in groups, will confirm the extent of their learning.

Habitats

Learning targets

The children should be able to:

1 ➤➤ say what a habitat is and be able to describe some habitats
2 ➤➤ observe and point out aspects of a habitat
3 ➤➤ observe a second habitat and make comparisons between different habitats

Before you start

Lesson preparation

Lesson 1

Posters, pictures, slides, video, CD-ROMs and books showing a wide range of habitats are needed. Some of these resources can be made into a class display before the lesson. Cut out and mount on card some pictures of animals and plants that are indigenous to the British Isles. On a large sheet of card, draw a landscape with some features that might present a range of habitats. A suggested landscape is shown on page 49. Photocopy Copymaster 37.

Lesson 2

Access to an appropriate local habitat is vital for this lesson. The children may be taken to a park, on to farm land (with the farmer's permission), to the beach or any habitat within easy reach of the school. Make a point of visiting the location prior to the children's visit so that you can make notes about the terrain, the plants and the animals that are likely to live there. Extra adult help will be required to supervise groups of children. Photocopy Copymaster 38.

Lesson 3

A visit out of school should be arranged for this lesson. The visit should be to a location with natural habitats different from the habitat seen in Lesson 2. If it proves difficult to arrange this, seek out museums with a natural history section, which will have detailed information about specific creatures and plants and where they live, and arrange for the children to go there. You should make a point of visiting the museum or natural location before the visit by the children in order to set it up for them and ensure that it is properly focused. Museum staff may be available to help the children. Parental permission and extra adult help will also be required. If appropriate, photocopy Copymaster 38 again for the children.

Investigations

Secondary sources giving details of chosen habitats in other part of the world and books and other information about some wild animals common to the British Isles are needed.

Health and safety

As is always the case when visiting locations outside school, be mindful of the children's safety and take care of the local environment. Make special provision for children with plant or animal allergies or hay fever.

Teaching the lessons

Lesson 1 ①

Vocabulary

Animal, habitat, look, observe, plant; the names for the specific animals and plants in the resources used

Introduction 10min

▦ Show the class display to the children and talk about the fact that there are a wide variety of different places where animals and plants live. Point out and name some of the animals and plants and where they live.

Activities 25min

👤 Give each child a copy of **Copymaster 37** and invite them to draw a creature that they think lives in each of the locations shown there.

▦ Using the mounted pictures of plants and animals and the large card landscape drawing, ask the children to suggest where each of the plants and animals might live. Using sticky tape or Blu-Tack®, stick the pictures of the animals and plants in the appropriate places on the drawing.

children may have seen few creatures and those may be only mini-beasts).

Lesson 3 ③

Vocabulary
Words related to the senses, words associated with field skills, such as observe and concentrate; the names of some of the plants, creatures and landscape features associated with the location visited

Introduction 10 min
Set up some notions in the children's minds about what will be expected of them during this lesson or visit.

Activities 30 min
As in Lesson 2, allow the children to explore the habitat in their groups with adult help and talk about what they see.

Bring the children together to give them a chance to talk about some of their first impressions of the work they have been doing.

Closing the lesson 15 min
With the children's help, compile a list of plants and other creatures for a particular habitat and compare this list with the plants and animals discussed in Lesson 2.

After the lessons

Homework
The children can look for a mini-habitat in their own garden, under a hedge or in a relative's garden. Even a window box may support creatures like ants, spiders and earthworms. Warn the children to observe safety rules, not to handle plants or small creatures and to wash their hands after work in the garden.

Investigations
Choose a location in another part of the world and help the children to research the animals and plants that live there, for example, Antarctica, the African plains, the Amazonian rainforest.

Ask the children to choose a wild animal common to the British Isles, for example, the hedgehog, and from what they can find out about its life and what it eats, they can determine the kinds of places in which it might live.

Assessment
Use the drawings and written work that the children have done and consider their conduct and contribution to practical work to determine how they are mastering scientific skills of observation, description, explanation and comparison.

Closing the lesson 5 min
Hold up Copymaster 37 and discuss the features in the pictures which give clues to the kinds of creatures that might live there. Explain that the word we use for the place where particular plants and animals live is 'habitat' and that the children will be moving on to work in specific habitats in the next two lessons.

Lesson 2 ②

Vocabulary
Words related to the senses; words associated with field skills, such as observe and concentrate; the names of some of the plants, creatures and landscape features associated with the location visited

Introduction 10 min
Check through with the children the purposes of the visit, what they are expected to do and the rules for their own safety and for care of the local environment.

Activities 40 min
Allow the children to go off in groups with a supervising adult to look round the habitat and talk about what they see.

Bring all the children together if this is possible and review some of the things they have seen.

Give each child a copy of **Copymaster 38** so that they can make a record of some of their experiences.

Closing the lesson 5 min
List for the children the key features of the habitat and some of the creatures that may live there (the

Sensing

Learning targets

The children should be able to:

1 ➡➡ explore and describe what different materials feel like
2 ➡➡ explore and describe what different materials look like
3 ➡➡ sort out materials, giving criteria for the sorts

Before you start

Lesson preparation

Lesson 1

Obtain at least ten card cartons like those in which groceries are delivered to supermarkets. Cut a hole in one side of each one, through which a child can put a hand, and seal and secure the other sides of the box. Collect as wide a range of samples of materials as possible, including natural and factory-made objects, for example, expanded polystyrene such as a food tray or cup, rigid plastic such as vinyl tiles or food boxes, others sorts of plastic such as bubble wrap or disposable bags, splinter-free wood, different types of card including corrugated cardboard, carpet samples, pebbles and rock samples, and a metal ruler. Put them into the cartons before the lesson so that the children cannot see them. These can be placed round the room.

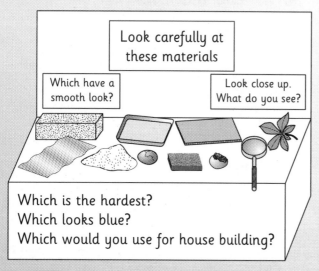

Look carefully at these materials

Which have a smooth look?

Look close up. What do you see?

Which is the hardest?
Which looks blue?
Which would you use for house building?

Lesson 2

Create a workshop display so that samples are arranged round the room. You can use the same samples that you used in Lesson 1 and include others that have a distinctive appearance, for example, rocks with crystalline structures. The workshop setting should be manageable providing there are at least as many samples as there are children in the class (to ensure that this is the case, duplicates of some samples can be used). Photocopy Copymaster 39.

Lesson 3

Put similar sets of samples into a number of boxes corresponding to the number of work groups in the class. In addition, have a 'master' box containing samples of the same materials that are as large as possible. Photocopy Copymaster 40.

Investigations

Gather a selection of samples of different materials. These can include some of those used in the lessons and will vary according to the investigation you wish the children to carry out. Resources required will also depend on the nature of the investigation but if they are those suggested below, the following will be required: kitchen scouring pads or sandpaper, measuring jugs, water and a suitable location to pour it.

Health and safety

Take care to choose materials that are safe to handle. Ensure that the children wash their hands after touching the materials. When children are close to dusty samples, for example, goggles or masks may be required. You should refer to current safety guidelines before starting these lessons.

Teaching the lessons

Lesson 1 ①

Vocabulary

All the words the children use to describe how the materials feel, for example, bumpy, hard, rough, soft, slippery, smooth, spongy, squashy

Introduction 10 min

▦ Hold up two samples that have different textures, for example, a velvet cushion and a block of wood. In discussion with the children, establish that we use our sense of touch to detect how things feel and that texture is the word we use to describe it. Invite two children in turn to feel the items and tell the rest of the class how they think the materials feel. Use these words to start the word list.

Activities 20min

👤 Ask the children to visit all the cartons positioned round the room and take turns to handle the items they contain without looking inside. If the children are assigned a box in twos or threes and asked to move round the room in the same direction, there should not be too long a queue at each box.

▦ Call the class together and ask the children if they can remember how the contents of each box felt and record their new words in the word list.

Closing the lesson 5min

▦ Offer round some additional material samples, asking children to describe how they feel, while looking at them.

Lesson 2 ②

Vocabulary

All the words in the list relating to texture that the children helped to compile in the first lesson; the names of all the material samples, including everyday and scientific names where appropriate; add all the words used in the lesson and check that it includes a wide range of colour words and words such as curved, granular, gritty, lumpy, sharp, shiny, smooth

Introduction 10min

▦ Take two or three samples from the workshop display before the lesson begins. Without showing them to the children, ask the children to close their eyes and be ready to make a picture in their mind's eye. Describe as fully as possible the appearance of one of the samples. When you have given them sufficient information, ask them to open their eyes. Show the material to the children. Invite them to say how their mental picture differed from the actual sample, then try the same game with another sample. Finally, ask a child to come and describe a third sample. Create a word list on a large sheet of paper, showing all the words you and the children have used.

Activities 25min

👥 Divide the children into groups and ask them to visit all the workshop sites and talk about all the materials they find. Circulate among the groups, stimulating the children into finding a wide range of words to describe the appearance of the materials.

👤 Give each child a copy of **Copymaster 39** and allow them to choose three different samples to draw and describe. You may wish them to do more than three.

Closing the lesson 5min

▦ Discuss with the children the words they have used to describe texture and appearance. Invite some of the children to read their descriptions aloud.

Lesson 3 ③

Vocabulary

Colour, group, put together, sort, texture, use; words the children use to justify their groupings

Introduction 10min

▦ Open the master box of samples. Take out all the samples and put them on a table where all the children will be able to see them. Put some of the samples together. Ask the children why they think you have grouped these particular samples (you may choose to group them on the basis of colour, texture or a property such as softness or shininess). Point out that they are going to have the chance to group materials according to a criterion that they choose for themselves.

Activities 20min

👥 Divide the class into groups and give each group a box of materials. Allow time for each child to complete a different 'sort' which their group can then explain. Offer support to those children who find the task difficult and, for the groups who work fast, set up an additional 'sort' yourself that they have to explain.

👥 Give every child a copy of **Copymaster 40** and ask them to record the sort they did.

Closing the lesson 5min

▦ Present the children with a feature or property of materials and ask them to suggest which materials might belong to that set. Here are some suggested properties: brittleness, bendiness, crumbliness, elasticity, hardness, rigidity, roughness, smoothness, squashiness.

After the lessons

Homework

With parental help, the children can make their own small collections of materials in the house and garden. These can be brought to school and displayed by the children themselves. The samples will also support further discussion of the properties of materials.

Investigations

Invite the children to place a selection of material samples in order, according to particular properties, for example:

Does it crumble? Supply kitchen scouring pads or sandpaper for the children to use on the samples. (Examples include brick, chalk, sandstone.)

Does it shine? (Examples include coal, cooking foil, steel.)

Does it absorb water? Supply measuring jugs, water and provide a suitable location to pour water. (Examples include sandstone, soap, wood.)

Assessment

The chief source of assessment data here is what the children say, the judgements they make and the vocabulary they use. Their written and practical work also provide information about their mastery of concepts related to the scientific skills of observation and reasoning and facts related to the properties discernible from looking at and handling materials.

Is it magnetic or non-magnetic?

Learning targets

The children should be able to:

1 ➤➤ explore the effects of a magnet

2 ➤➤ understand that some things are attracted to a magnet and some are not

3 ➤➤ predict and test which materials are attracted to a magnet

Before you start

Lesson preparation

Lesson 1

The equipment listed on Copymaster 41 will be required for each pair. This equipment comprises one card strip, two pieces of card, eight paper clips, two pairs of scissors, two magnets, two sticks and two pieces of string. The children will also need colouring pencils or felt-tip pens. Make enough photocopies of Copymaster 41 to give one to each pair of children.

Lesson 2

Assemble several boxes of items which can be tested with a magnet for each work group in the class. Each box should contain all the portable items shown on Copymaster 42, namely a 2p coin, bottle top, button, card, chalk, clothes peg, cork, eraser, feather, flowerpot, food tin, key, leaf, marble, paper, paper clip, paper fastener, pebble, pencil, plastic, ribbon, ring, rubber band, scissors, screw, string, wax crayon, wood. Additionally, the children will need access to a door handle and a lunch box. Photocopy Copymaster 42.

Lesson 3

Before the lesson, set up a display of metal items. An example display is shown in the Introduction to this lesson (page 53). You will need enough small magnets to give at least one to each pair of children. The box of items used in Lesson 2 can be used again.

Investigations

You will need pairs of tiny magnetic toys.

Health and safety

Warn the children that magnets should not be placed near watches, calculators, televisions, computers, computer disks or videos because magnetic fields have detrimental effects on them.

Teaching the lessons

Lesson 1 ①

Vocabulary

Attract, magnet, magnetic, pull towards

Introduction ⏱ 5min

▦ Explain to the children that you would like them to work in twos and create a magnetic fishing game. Hold up a copy of **Copymaster 41** and talk it through with the children. Arrange for the equipment to be given out to pairs of children.

Activities ⏱ 25min

👥 Give each pair of children a copy of Copymaster 41. Allow them to make their game, helping those children who find it difficult to attach their magnet to the string.

👥 Allow the children to play the game.

Closing the lesson ⏱ 10min

▦ Discuss with the children their experiences. Ask questions to consolidate what the children have learned, for example:

What happened when the magnet dangled over a paper-clip fish?

What happened when the magnet touched a fish without a paper clip attached to it?

Did the fishing string work without a magnet on the end?

How many fish attached themselves to the magnet at the same time?

Lesson 2 ① ②

Vocabulary

Attract, magnet, magnetic, metal, plastic, pull towards, test, wood; the names of other materials and objects which children use in the lesson

Introduction `5min`

▦ Remind the children of their work in Lesson 1. Repeat words like magnet and attract to check that they understand what will be expected of them in the coming lesson.

Activities `30min`

◆◆ Divide the class into groups and allow each group to have access to a box of items and a magnet. They can all have several turns at finding out which objects in the box are attracted to the magnet.

▦ Call the class together and check that every child has had a turn at using the magnet. Allow some children to talk about what happened.

◑◐ Give each child a copy of **Copymaster 42**. In their work groups, the children can test the objects with the magnet again and record the results.

Closing the lesson `10min`

▦ Ask individual children to tell the class about the record they made. Ask who has an explanation for what happened. See if the children can deduce that some things are attracted to a magnet and that these things are all made of metal.

Lesson 3 ① ② ③

Vocabulary

Attract, copper, magnet, magnetic, metal, pull towards, shiny, silver, steel, test; the names of other metals that arise in the lesson

Introduction `5min`

▦ Ask the children to name something attracted by a magnet and talk about what happens and what they think the item is made from. Draw the children's attention to the display to help their answers. Above right is an example display.

Activities `30min`

▟ Place the children in pairs and ask them to explore the whole room, predicting which things will be attracted by a magnet. They should start to make a record, showing their predictions. Then give each pair of children a magnet so that they can test their predictions. Warn the children not to place the magnet near watches, calculators, other electrical equipment and computer disks.

▮ Ask the children to complete their own picture or word charts, showing their predictions, the things they tested and which ones were attracted to the magnet.

Closing the lesson `10min`

▦ Review the children's findings with them. Compare a number of ways of setting out the information. Confirm with the children that the things attracted to a magnet are made of metal but that not all metals are attracted to a magnet.

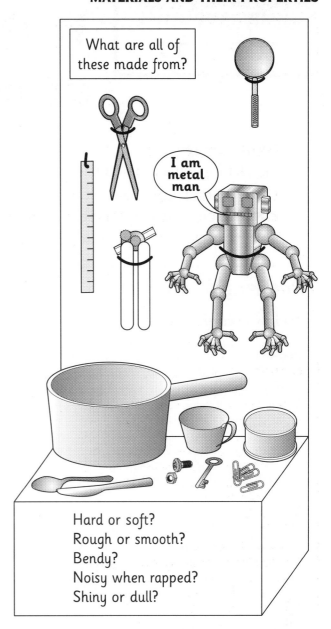

What are all of these made from?

I am metal man

Hard or soft?
Rough or smooth?
Bendy?
Noisy when rapped?
Shiny or dull?

After the lessons

Homework

Ask the children to find out about the strength of the refrigerator magnets they have at home. We usually put a piece of paper (a shopping list or reminder) behind the magnet. They can see how many pieces of paper the magnet will 'work' through.

Investigations

Offer the children a pair of little magnetic toys to explore. These are sold in animal pairs (for example, ladybirds or elephants) and can be made to jiggle by moving one around the other. The children can find out when it is possible to get the creatures to touch and when they move apart.

Assessment

The children's involvement in the practical activities, their use of key words such as 'magnet' and 'attract' and their written work should serve to indicate their understanding of magnetic properties.

Transparency and other properties

Learning targets

The children should be able to:

1 ➤➤ distinguish between transparent, translucent and opaque

2 ➤➤ explore whether materials are elastic

3 ➤➤ observe and record a test of strength of a material

Before you start

Lesson preparation

Lesson 1

Create a display of materials with varying degrees of transparency, from transparent to opaque. Place four different samples of materials into topic boxes for each work group in the class. The children need access to other parts of the school during this lesson. It would also be useful to have extra adult supervision for groups walking round school. Photocopy Copymasters 43 and 44.

Lesson 2

Assemble a box of ten samples for each work group. These should include, for example, a plastic ruler, a woollen sleeve, some brown paper, a carrier bag, an elastic band, a tea towel, leather, a J-cloth®, and tissue paper.

Lesson 3

Sample materials of different strengths are required here. Some suggested examples include card, cotton fabric, nylon, paper, wood and wool. Set up two breeze blocks or bricks as shown below. Choose a range of sample materials which will withstand a weight without deflecting, materials that will stretch without breaking and materials that will break under the weight. Before the lesson, experiment attaching samples to the bricks using strong tape and by other methods.

Investigations

Examples of different kinds of plastics used in food packaging and a range of plastic toys are required.

Health and safety

Children need to take care in handling materials and be aware of the fact that the edges of paper can cut and that pulling fabrics can sear the skin. Some children may have skins that are sensitive to particular materials. The edge of a broken piece of plastic can be sharp.

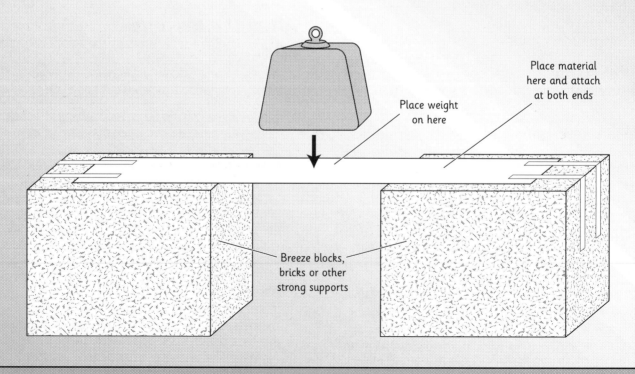

Place weight on here

Place material here and attach at both ends

Breeze blocks, bricks or other strong supports

Teaching the lessons

Lesson 1

Vocabulary

Clear, look, obscured, opaque, see, translucent, transparent

Introduction |10 min|

Use the display of materials with different degrees of transparency to introduce the vocabulary. Hold up each sample and place a book or hand behind it. Allow the children to look through it and comment on what they see. Give them the key words to use. Here is a sample display.

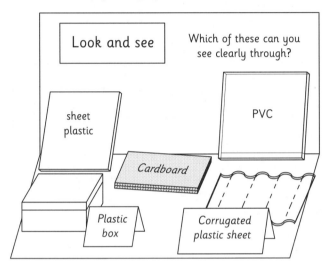

Look and see

Which of these can you see clearly through?

sheet plastic

PVC

Cardboard

Plastic box

Corrugated plastic sheet

Activities |30 min|

Give out the topic boxes and copies of **Copymaster 43** to each work group. Allow the children to complete the task by holding up each sample, trying to look through it and drawing it in the appropriate box on the copymaster. If the samples are named, the children can also write in the name.

Ask the children, in groups, to look round the school and find examples of transparent, translucent and opaque materials.

If time permits, the children can record on **Copymaster 44** some of the materials they found on their walk.

Closing the lesson |10 min|

Allow the groups to report back to the class about the materials they found.

Lesson 2 ②

Vocabulary

Break, elastic, longer, pull, rank, stretch, stretchy, tear

Introduction |10 min|

Pick out some samples from one of the boxes and demonstrate, by pulling the material, that some things are more elastic than others. Discuss with the children what is meant by 'rank order'.

Activities |20 min|

Divide the class into groups. Ask them to take all the samples out of their boxes and try each one to see how stretchy it is, then agree a rank order starting with the most elastic.

The children should now all write or draw the materials in the ranking they have assigned to them.

Closing the lesson |10 min|

Review what the children have done and compare the rankings of different groups. Point out that if a sample tears when stretched or does not return to its original shape after stretching, it is because it has passed a point beyond which it cannot be stretched further and this point is different for different materials.

Lesson 3 ③

Vocabulary

Strength, strong, weight

Introduction |5 min|

Explain to the class that they are going to watch an experiment that you are going to do. If it is appropriate, erect a screen between the front table and where the children are sitting because the weight may plummet to the table when put on a fragile material.

Activities |25 min|

Ask the children to predict what will happen when the weight is put on each of the materials. Then try the experiment and let the children watch what happens. Discuss any unexpected results. Ask individual children to try to explain the results.

Invite the children to draw and write about what they have observed.

Closing the lesson |5 min|

Produce a few more materials and ask the children what they think would happen if the experiment was repeated with these.

After the lessons

Homework

The children can do a survey of their homes to see which windows are transparent and which are translucent.

Investigations

Invite the children to look for or investigate the bendiness of some materials. These can include a range of plastics used in food packaging and in toys.

Assessment

The children's attention to the lesson and their contributions should provide evidence of understanding.

Naming materials

Learning targets

The children should be able to:

1 ➤➤ give the names of some materials

2 ➤➤ distinguish some materials that are natural, some that are artificial and some that are processed from natural materials

3 ➤➤ identify which materials are found in objects made from a number of materials

4 ➤➤ distinguish the features common to differing categories of material

Before you start

Lesson preparation

Lesson 1

Set up a three-part display entitled 'Wood, Plastic, Metal' and assemble at least six examples in each part of the display. Here are some examples.

Wood	Plastic	Metal
Branch	Box	Biscuit tin
Broom (stick)	Plastic bucket	Coat hook
Clog	Cup	Desk lamp
Wooden clothes peg	Dustpan	Drinks can
Doll's house	Felt-tip pen	Kitchen tool
Door knob	Goldfish bowl	Saucepan
Pencil	Packaging	Spanner
Wooden ruler	Shopping bag	Spoon
Stool	Spoon	Toy
Toy	Toy	Triangle or bells

Additional items from the three categories will also be needed for the children to conduct sorting activities. These should be placed in a box before the lesson. Photocopy Copymaster 45.

Lesson 2

Make sets of three cards illustrating natural materials, the intermediate processed materials and the final products we use. Here are some suggestions.

Natural	Intermediate	Product
Tree	Plank	Boat
Tree	Paper	Book
Gemstone in rock	Cut gemstone	Ring with gemstone setting
Natural hard rock	Cut stones	Part of a building
Lump of chalk		Classroom chalk
The sea		Canister of sea salt

Three collections of items are also required for this lesson. They should comprise natural materials in their natural state, synthetic materials and products processed from natural materials. Here are some examples.

Natural	Synthetic	Processed
Bamboo	Cellophane	Basket
Chalk	Plastics	Bottle cork
Clay		Cork mat
Coal		Metal bottle cap
Cork		Paper or book
Sponge		Pencil
Tree twig		Rubber band

Set out at random round the room at least six natural materials and objects made from them. (The children will need access to the things and to match them up). Photocopy Copymaster 46.

Lesson 3

A collection of items all made from more than one material is required for this lesson. The children could be asked to bring in items for display. Here are some suggestions: computer, hairdryer, photograph frame, schoolbag, shoe, toys, upholstered stool.

Investigations

Access to the built environment, including buildings from a range of centuries.

Health and safety

As with all the topics involving materials, children should be aware of their properties and take care of themselves and others when near, for example, sharp edges and heavy objects.

Teaching the lessons

Lesson 1 ①

Vocabulary

Metal, plastic, wood; the names of the samples on display and that the children mention

Introduction `10min`

View and describe the three-part display, then invite individual children to take an item from the box and add it to the appropriate part of the display.

Activities `20min`

Put a mixed pile of items on a table in front of the class. Ask a child to sort the items according to what they are made from. Ask a second child to comment on the resulting groups. Discuss contentious decisions with the class. Conduct the same activity once or twice more, using a new selection of items each time and with different children.

Give each child a copy of **Copymaster 45** and ask them to draw a set of objects in each of the three sets.

Closing the lesson `5min`

Hold up individual items and ask the children what they are made of. Mention again names of woods and plastics if appropriate and metals such as aluminium, chromium, copper and steel.

Lesson 2 ① ②

Vocabulary

Made, metal, natural, plastic, process, wood; the names of other materials

Introduction `10min`

Explain to the children that the things around us in our everyday lives include natural materials which are just as they are found on or in the Earth. There are also some materials which do not exist naturally and are made in factories, while others begin as natural materials and are processed in some way to make the things we need. Take up individual items from the collection to illustrate the points being made.

Activities `25min`

Use one of the sets of cards illustrating natural materials, the intermediate processed materials and the final products we use. Show the children the pictures in a jumbled order. Ask them in which order they think the pictures should go. Then use another set of cards and recruit the help of a child to hold them up and establish their order.

Give each child a copy of **Copymaster 46** and ask them to go round the room and find the materials and objects which go together. They can then draw them on the copymaster.

Closing the lesson `5min`

Review the work the children have done on Copymaster 46.

Lesson 3 ③ ④

Vocabulary

The names of all the materials in the items on display; all the words the children use in their descriptions

Introduction `10min`

Pick up one of the items from the display and ask the children what they think it is made from. List on the board the materials they name. Ask individual children to pick up other items and point to and say what they were made from.

Activities `25min`

Divide the class into groups and give each work group two items made from more than one material and ask them to identify the materials. Visit the groups to find out how they are getting on.

Ask each group to tell the class what their items are made from.

Draw on the board a number of little pictures denoting some of the features of the categories of materials. Here are some suggestions.

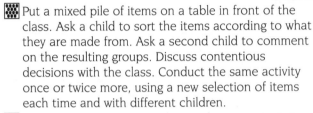

shiny	hard	fluffy	soft	bendy/springy

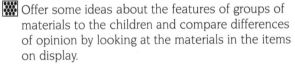

sharp	rough	smooth	dull	stretchy

Ask the children to write the words 'wood', 'plastic' and 'metal' in their books. They can then draw little pictures to show what they think are the most common features of these groups of materials.

Closing the lesson `5min`

Offer some ideas about the features of groups of materials to the children and compare differences of opinion by looking at the materials in the items on display.

After the lessons

Homework

Ask the children to draw their favourite toys and write underneath what they are made of.

Investigations

Using extra adult help for supervision, take the children out to look at homes, bridges, office buildings and street structures such as lamps and post boxes. Talk about the materials used in their construction.

Assessment

The children's contributions to class discussions, their practical work and their written work should provide evidence of their learning.

What do we use it for?

Learning targets

The children should be able to:

1 ➤➤ say how we use some materials

2 ➤➤ understand the importance of different materials in our everyday lives

3 ➤➤ choose materials for different uses

Before you start

Lesson preparation

Lesson 1

Pictures, catalogues, advertisements and posters depicting a wide range of objects are needed. Set these up as a frieze round the room at the children's eye-level. Some sample materials in their natural state along with things made from them will also be needed. Below are some examples. Photocopy **Copymaster 47**.

Natural material	Product
Rock with crystalline structure	Necklace with crystal beads
Rubber (note that much of it is now synthetic)	Carpet underlay/sports pumps
Coconut with fibres attached	Coconut mat
Washed sheep's wool	Woollen jumper

Lesson 2

Video footage of children in their daily lives would be helpful in this lesson. These can be snippets of home videos or episodes from children's television programmes.

Set up an arts workshop for the children to paint draw and do collage work.

Lesson 3

Photocopy Copymasters 48 and 49.

Investigations

Materials that can be cut into half-metre squares are needed for this lesson, including, for example, pieces of cotton, nylon, plastic, paper. A supply of at least four kinds of paper handkerchiefs is also needed.

Health and safety

As with all work with materials, ask the children to take care. Watch out for skin allergies related to wool and other fabrics.

Teaching the lessons

Lesson 1   ① ②

Vocabulary

The names of the objects depicted in the pictures in the frieze; the names of a wide range of materials

Introduction   `10min`

Point to some of the pictures in the frieze and discuss with the children the kinds of materials involved. Ask key questions such as, for example:

What is it?

What is it made from?

Where does this material come from? (Answers may include the ground, the sea, a tree, a plant.)

What has been done to this material to make something we use? (Answers may include, for example, that it has been cut up, changed in shape, pulled out, squeezed.)

Why do you think this material has been used?

Activities   `20min`

Give each child a copy of **Copymaster 47** to complete.

Show the children the sample materials and invite them to say which objects they are made into and why these materials have been used.

Closing the lesson   `10min`

Name some of the features of a material and ask the children 'What would it be good for?'. For example, a material that is strong and hard might make good buildings, furniture or machinery, while one that is soft and stretchy would make comfortable clothing.

Lesson 2   ②

Vocabulary

Words related to the activities the children do; the objects they use and the materials from which they are made

Introduction   `5min`

Ask a child to tell the class about their activities throughout a day. Then begin the sequence again, with you adding some of the things they use and what they might be made from.

Activities   `30min`

Watch the video footage with the children. This can

be stopped to point out all the objects the child uses and the materials from which they are made.

Divide the class into groups and ask the children to make pictures of children using objects made from different materials. Each group could use a different medium and work on a group effort or in pairs. For example, they could be given poster paints, felt-tip pens or collage fabrics. If you wish, the children could incorporate real objects in their pictures.

- coloured paper or paint
- metal
- real spoon anchored to the page (curve arm around it)
- real cereal
- paper bowl

Rashid is eating his breakfast with a spoon made of steel.

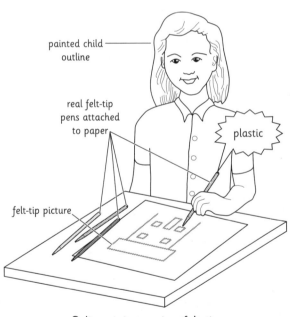

- painted child outline
- real felt-tip pens attached to paper
- plastic
- felt-tip picture

Selina enjoys using felt-tip pens. They are made of plastic.

Closing the lesson   [5 min]

Review all the work the children have done, pointing up the wide variety of materials we put to a range of uses in our everyday lives.

Lesson 3   (3)

Vocabulary

As wide a range as possible of names of materials and their properties

Introduction   [5 min]

Remind the children that we can choose what material to use to make something from, according to what we know about it. Ask the children why we do not use materials in the following ways: paper to make knives, chocolate to make cars, clay to make chairs. Ask the children to think of some inappropriate ways of using materials.

Activities   [30 min]

Divide the class into groups and give each group a copy of **Copymaster 48** with a list of things which need to be 'invented' or made, for example:

List 1	List 2	List 3	List 4
Bath tap	Bath plug	Bed	Clock
Bracelet	Curtain	Bicycle tyre	Hot-water bottle
Egg whisk	Drinks bottle	Box	Pen
Pillow	Go-kart	Picture frame	Radio
Slipper	Key	Purse	Scissors
Sports bag	Key-ring	Stepladder	Waste bin

Give the children time to decide amongst themselves which of the materials in the picture would be most appropriate to make these things and why.

Allow the groups to take turns to tell the other children what they would use to make their items.

Give each child a copy of **Copymaster 49** so that they can record what materials they would use.

Closing the lesson   [5 min]

Review the children's work on the copymasters.

After the lessons

Homework

Give the children a list of things to think about, for example:

What would you choose to use to make something to:

carry a drink?	carry a baby?	carry shopping?
sit on?	climb on?	stand on?
use to wipe clean?	use to mop up?	use to remove dust?
keep you warm?	help you cool off?	
tidy your hair?	clean your teeth?	

Investigations

Help the children to devise an experiment to determine what they think will make a suitable parachute material. Allow the children to make toy parachutes, try them out and evaluate their choices.

Ask the children to devise a way of finding out which paper handkerchief soaks up most water. Run the experiment, then try it as a demonstration and ask for the children's comments on the results. Help them suggest why they got the results that they did.

Assessment

The children's participation in all the classroom activities will support your assessment.

Shape changes

Learning targets

The children should be able to:

1 ➤➤ try changing the shape of materials
2 ➤➤ observe the effect of air and the effects of external forces in changing the shape of some materials
3 ➤➤ use shape changing in cooking

Before you start

Lesson preparation

Lesson 1

You will need Silly Putty®, for a demonstration. Play dough or air-drying clay (for example Newclay®) in quantities that allow each child to have a blob are also required for this lesson. Play dough can be made up using the following recipe (proportions may need slight adjustment to achieve the appropriate degree of elasticity). Mix together flour, salt and water in these proportions: one cup of salt and one cup of water to two cups of flour and two tablespoons of cooking oil. Knead all the ingredients together to make a stretchy dough that holds its shape. One or two little rubber faces into which fingers are inserted at the back would be useful to end the lesson. Photocopy Copymaster 50.

Lesson 2

Balloons and a balloon pump, foam and sponge balls and party blowers which wind out when inflated are needed for this lesson. The children will also need access to the hall or PE room for part of the lesson. Photocopy Copymaster 51.

Lesson 3

Ingredients and tools for a simple biscuit recipe are required, including aprons, balances, bowls, round-tipped knives, sleeve protectors, small boards for rolling icing or dough, small rolling pins and spoons. Access to the oven will be required. After the biscuits are cooked, it will be necessary to roll out icing and other decorations. Extra adult help will be required to assist the children in preparing the dough and in using the oven.

Investigations

No special resources are required, though the children may need access to other parts of the school.

Health and safety

Warn children of the dangers of hot ovens, oven doors, cooking trays and electricity. Remind them also of the rules of hygiene for cooking, ensuring that they have washed their hands, have tied back their hair and are wearing clean aprons.

Teaching the lessons

Lesson 1 ➊

Vocabulary

Bend, change, material, pull, push, shape, stretch, turn, twist

Introduction   10min

▓ Take up the Silly Putty®, and show the children how this particular material can be made to change shape by means of push and pull forces.

Activities   25min

♣ Divide the class into groups and give some of them a blob of air-drying clay and give the others play dough. Invite the children to twist, bend, stretch and distort their modelling medium as much as possible, then to create a model with it, which can be air dried if clay or oven dried if play dough.

👤 Give each child a copy of **Copymaster 50** so that they can record the work they have done.

Closing the lesson   5min

▓ Look with the children at some of the completed models and discuss the changes of shape that have taken place in the original blob of material.

Lesson 2 ②

Vocabulary

Air, bend, change, material, paper, pull, push, rubber, shape, sponge, stretch, turn, twist

Introduction ⟨10min⟩

Show the children the shape and size of a balloon before it has air pumped into it. Using the balloon pump, inflate the balloon and let them see the changes that take place as it is progressively inflated. Talk about the shape and size changes to the material as the increasing air pressure inside the balloon forces the material to adopt a different shape and size.

Activities ⟨25min⟩

Take the class into the hall for a short PE session involving soft foam balls. Allow them to experiment with bouncing and catching the balls. Then call the children together and ask them what they believe happens to the ball as it strikes the ground, a bat or the hand. Ask questions such as:

What shape is the ball?

How do you think the shape of the ball changes when it hits your hand?

What about when it hits the ground?

 Give each child a copy of **Copymaster 51** for them to complete.

Closing the lesson ⟨10min⟩

Try out a party blower in front of the children. Ask them to say what is happening to the overall shape of the blower due to the force of the air being blown through it.

Lesson 3 ③

Vocabulary

Bend, change, pull, push, shape, stretch, turn, twist

Introduction ⟨15min⟩

The purpose here is to show the change of shape imposed on the biscuit dough and to set the scene for a discussion of other kinds of change in materials. Point out to the children that they will be making biscuits and that they should think about the changes in shape that they are making to the mix.

Make up a small quantity of the biscuit mix while the children watch. Remind the children of all the kitchen rules of hygiene and point out how the dough can be changed in shape. Cut out biscuits ready for placing in the oven.

Activities ⟨20min⟩

Divide the class into groups. Ask two groups to make biscuits while the remaining children roll out the icing for the biscuits. With adult help, they can roll out the dough and cut the biscuits using a round-tipped knife, a card shape they have made or a cookie cutter.

Make a written record of the work carried out in making the biscuits.

Closing the lesson ⟨10min⟩

It would be ideal if the lesson can be extended so that every group has the chance to roll out and 'change the shape of' their icing to fit their biscuits. Discuss with the children the experience they have had and ask them to remember what they can about the biscuit dough when it was first made, when it was ready for cooking and after cooking as these ideas will come up again in subsequent topics.

After the lessons

Homework

Ask the children to find a simple cake or biscuit recipe that they would like to try. Ask them to bring their recipes to school so that some of the recipes can be tried (in experiments to show permanent change) and added to a class recipe book.

Investigations

Ask the children to look for uses to which we put materials because they change shape. These may include bungee cord, cushions, elastic bands (and straps on things like swimming goggles) and mattresses.

Assessment

Children's participation levels and their contributions to class work should indicate their understanding.

Heating and cooling: changing back

Learning targets

The children should be able to:

1 ➤➤ observe what happens when chocolate and jelly are warmed, then cooled
2 ➤➤ conduct an experiment using ice lollies
3 ➤➤ examine what happens when some liquids are cooled

Before you start

Lesson preparation

Lesson 1

The following are needed: aprons, boiling water, bowls including some heatproof bowls, chocolate (white, milk or plain), chocolate moulds, a pan to which boiling water can be added, small jelly moulds, table jelly, a tray on which to set out the moulds and washing facilities. Access to a refrigerator will also be necessary if time is short. Photocopy Copymaster 52.

Lesson 2

A box of at least six ice lollies are needed. These can be made well ahead of time in lolly moulds and placed in the kitchen freezer. The children will need the appropriate equipment to carry out the experiments which they devise, possibly plates to set the lollies on and timers. Photocopy Copymaster 53.

Lesson 3

The following are needed: Freeze Pops®, or similar 'frozen drinks', ice cubes and frozen orange juice. Access to a freezer is necessary.

Investigations

Depending on the investigations that the children undertake, they will require boiling water, bowls, chocolate, ice lollies, jelly, jugs, plates and equipment that individual experiments may demand as well as access to a refrigerator.

Health and safety

Remind children constantly of the need for scrupulous attention to hygiene, especially if any of the foods are to be eaten afterwards (it is anticipated that the children will want to eat the chocolate, at least). Check that none of the children have allergies to the colourings or flavourings in lollies.

Teaching the lessons

Lesson 1 ①

Vocabulary

Boiling water, chocolate, heat, heatproof, melt, set

Introduction 5min

▦ This lesson may be best carried out in two parts because the children will need to view the chocolate and jelly once it has reset later in the day. Check that the children know some of the key vocabulary to be used in this lesson, including melt and set. Explain that you are going to see what changes happen to chocolate and jelly when they are heated then cooled.

Activities 45min

▦ Using a bowl standing in a pan of hot water, melt the chocolate in the bowl. Allow all the children to observe what happens to the chocolate. Take care not to splash water into the chocolate. Ask the children to comment on what changes have taken place, for example, in consistency or colour of the chocolate. Then tip the melted chocolate into moulds, having first asked the children what they think will happen next.

▤ Allow the children time to complete the 'chocolate flow chart' on **Copymaster 52**.

▦ Show the children what happens when the jelly cubes are stirred into boiling water. Encourage them to talk about what occurs. Place some of the melted jelly in a refrigerator and examine it later in the day.

▤ Ask the children to complete their work on Copymaster 52.

Closing the lesson 5min

▦ Review the key ideas raised here, including the observation that when warmed the substances became liquid and when cooled they can no longer be poured.

Lesson 2 ②

Vocabulary

Ice, liquid, melt, water

Introduction 5 min

Find out what the children know about the relationship between ice and water by asking questions like the following:

Where do we find ice?

Where does water come from?

What is ice?

What happens when ice is left in a glass?

Activities 45 min

Show the children water in various containers (food colouring can be added to make it easier to see). Then look at some ice and continue the discussion begun in the introduction.

Divide the class into groups and invite each group to think about an experiment they would like to conduct on an ice lolly. Visit each group when they think they have a good idea. If the ideas are possible to try out, help each group to set up and begin their experiment. If they cannot think of an idea that can be carried through, invite them to observe and time the melting of a lolly. They can note, for example, whether it melts at one end first, how it changes shape and whether the rate of melting seems to be steady or whether it slows down or accelerates.

 Ask the children to write about their experiment on **Copymaster 53**.

Closing the lesson 5 min

Review the experiments by asking the children to talk about what problems they had and how these could be solved.

Lesson 3 ③

Vocabulary

Cold, cool, freeze, liquids, melt, set

Introduction 10 min

A day or two before the lesson, place in the school kitchen freezer samples of the fluids that you are going to show to the children. Begin the lesson by showing them the liquid versions of these at room temperature. Here are some examples: Freeze Pops®, or similar drinks that can be frozen, water in an ice-cube maker and orange juice. Check that the children have come across these.

Activities 25 min

Allow the children to handle the Freeze Pops®, ice-cube makers full of water and a jug of juice. Then ask what they think would happen if these were placed in the freezer. Visit the freezer and pull out the samples. Let the children examine them.

 With parental permission, allow every child to have a frozen Freeze Pop® to eat.

Closing the lesson 10 min

Review what happens when the liquids are placed in the freezer. Discuss why it is that neither ice-cube makers nor Freeze Pops® are full of liquid but when frozen the containers are completely full.

After the lessons

Homework

Invite the children to ask if they may make jelly at home with adult help and supervision.

Investigations

The children can try to devise and carry out experiments on some of these questions:

Which shape of chocolate bar is easier to break into pieces?

Why is chocolate harder to break when it comes straight from the refrigerator?

Does chocolate melt quicker in the hand than on a plate? Why is this so?

Another set of jellies can be made for the children to work on some of these questions:

What determines how fast a jelly sets?

Does a small jelly set quicker than a big jelly?

Does a small piece of jelly turn to liquid quicker in hot water than a large piece of jelly?

This set of questions can also be given to the children:

Why does a lolly sometimes fall off its stick?

How long does it take a lolly to melt?

Does the size or shape of the lolly affect melting time?

What happens when an ice lolly is put in water?

Assessment

Observe the concentration of the children and their contributions to the class work.

Heating and cooling: all change

Learning targets

The children should be able to:

1 ➡➡ observe that some things can be changed and the change is not reversible

2 ➡➡ carry out some baking as an example of a change that is not reversible

3 ➡➡ make a relief in plaster of Paris as an example of a change that is not reversible

Before you start

Lesson preparation

Lesson 1

You will need bread, a cooker, earthenware crockery and flowerpots, fresh eggs, low-fat spread, plates, round-tipped knives, a saucepan, a toaster and water. Photocopy Copymaster 54.

Lesson 2

You will need the ingredients for a simple cake recipe to be made as a demonstration or preferably for the children to make themselves. You will also need cake papers, an egg beater or egg whisk, patty tins and cooling grids. Photocopy Copymaster 55.

Here is a suggested recipe for fairy cakes.

Ingredients

110 g of caster sugar

110 g of fat

175 g of self-raising flour

2 beaten or whisked eggs

a little water

Method

Cream the sugar and fat, then fold in the flour and the beaten or whisked eggs. Place cake papers over the shapes in the patty tins and spoon a little of the mixture on to each cake paper. Place the tins in a hot oven and bake at 190 °C for 10–18 minutes. Allow the cakes to cool before removing them from the tins.

Lesson 3

You will need air-drying clay, plaster of Paris, a large bowl and cleaning equipment for this lesson, as well as dried beans, pasta, pebbles, shells and twigs. You will also need access to water and additional adult help with setting up the lesson. Ask each child to bring into school an empty margarine tub.

Investigations

You will need model-making kits that use moulds, candle-making kits, play dough and plastic/mosaic sets.

Health and safety

Remind the children about the hygiene rules in a kitchen. Take care with plaster of Paris as it sets rapidly and gets hot as it does so due to the exothermic chemical reaction between the gypsum and the water. Handle the dry plaster with care to avoid dust contamination. It is very important that mixing bowls are cleaned soon after use and excess plaster disposed of appropriately so that it does not block waste pipes when set.

Teaching the lessons

Lesson 1 ①

Vocabulary

Bake, boil, bread, change, change back, clay, cook, egg, oven, pot, toast

Introduction 10 min

▓ Point out to the children that there are materials that we can change but which will not change back, unlike chocolate, which can be made liquid and then solid again. Show the children the lump of clay along with the flowerpots and earthenware cups and bowls. Tell the children that these products started out as similar lumps of clay. Ask them to say what clay is like and check that they identify the following characteristics: malleable, soft and stretchy. Then allow the children to look at the flowerpots and crockery and investigate their characteristics which include brittleness, hardness and a fixed shaped. Discuss the fact that our crockery never changes into soft clay again.

Activities `25 min`

▦ Allow the children to examine some slices of bread. Toast some of the slices and make comparisons between the toasted and untoasted bread. Boil some eggs and compare these with a raw egg. If it is appropriate, mash the boiled egg and spread it on bite-sized pieces of toast for the children to eat.

👤 Give each child a copy of **Copymaster 54** to complete.

Closing the lesson `5 min`

▦ Remind the children that they have been looking at changes which are permanent and cannot be reversed.

Lesson 2 ②

Vocabulary

Bake, biscuit, cake, change, change back, cook, eggs, fat, flour, mixture, oven, spoon, sugar

Introduction `10 min`

▦ Begin the lesson by giving a demonstration of how to make the cake mixture. While the children watch you make the mixture, explain to them all the skills involved and what is being added to the mixture each time.

Activities `30 min`

◑ Divide the class into two groups. In order that every child in the class should have hands-on experience of cooking, allow half to do the cooking while the others make a record of the recipe and the method along with what they expect to happen when the cakes are cooked. Then swap the activities of the groups.

◑ Ask the children to make a record of the cooking experiment on **Copymaster 55**.

Closing the lesson `5 min`

▦ Review the work done during the lesson and ask the children to recall the appearance and consistency of the cake mixture before it was baked and what it looked like afterwards.

Lesson 3 ③

Vocabulary

Clay, change, cold, hard, heat, hot, liquid, plaster of Paris, runny, set, soft

Introduction `15 min`

▦ Demonstrate to the children what they are about to do. Take a blob of clay and make into a small, flattish slab. Press the slab into a margarine tub so that it fills the bottom of the tub. Take some beans, pasta shapes, twigs and other items and press them into the clay so that they make a dent but do not produce a hole. Remove the shaped items. Make up a small quantity of plaster of Paris, according to the

instructions on the packet. When mixed, tip the plaster into the margarine tub. Leave the tub in a safe place, untouched, until the plaster is completely hard.

Activities `25 min`

👤 Give every child the opportunity to make their shaped clay mould in their tub. Extra adult supervision would be invaluable here. The children should write their names on sticky labels and fix them to the outside of the tubs.

▦ Make up a quantity of plaster of Paris while the children watch. Immediately after mixing, tip the plaster into the children's moulds. Put aside the moulds to set and some hours later, or the following day, peel away the tubs and remove the clay to expose the plaster reliefs.

Closing the lesson `5 min`

▦ Ask the children to predict how their reliefs will look and feel. Discuss the idea that the change taking place in the mixture of plaster and water is one that cannot be reversed.

After the lessons

Homework

Give each child a blob of play dough. They can take it home to model and ask an adult to place it at the bottom of a very cool oven for an hour. The model can then be brought into school for painting and varnishing.

Investigations

Ask the children to look at a number of craft kits and decide whether they think that the changes made to the contents are reversible. If there is time, under supervision the children can try out some of these kits.

Kit	Reversible change?
Model-making with a mould	No
Candle-making	Yes
Play dough	No
Plastic/mosaic set	Yes

Assessment

Observe the children at work and listen to their contributions to the discussions.

Play safe

Learning targets

The children should be able to:

1 ➨➔understand that electrical points are dangerous
2 ➨➔say that some things around the home and school use electricity
3 ➨➔understand that all appliances need care because they are potentially harmful
4 ➨➔use some of the words needed when talking about electricity

Before you start

Lesson preparation

Lesson 1

It would be helpful if the parts of an electrical socket could be shown to the children. They can be bought from electrical suppliers. Put at least the following into a box: the plastic cover and switch for a socket, some electrical flex, a plug connected to the flex and a small screwdriver. Collect pictures from magazines of room interiors, including kitchens, halls, stairs, living rooms and bedrooms in which skirtings and worktops are in evidence so that places for electrical sockets can be indicated.

Lesson 2

Catalogue and magazine pictures of appliances from home, office and school. Photocopy Copymaster 56.

Lesson 3

Make a model appliance like a cooker or washing machine from junk modelling materials. Add all the appropriate details so that it can be used in the lesson.

Card strips on which to write important words would be helpful. Begin with words on cards, including burn, control, danger, electricity, flex, heat, hot, lead, off, on, plug and switch.

Homework

Photocopy Copymaster 57 to give to the children.

Investigations

Access to other parts of the school and extra adult supervision for groups of children would be useful here.

Health and safety

This topic is almost exclusively about safety issues and the children should be continually reminded not to touch electrical points or sockets or to tamper with appliances, even though they are learning about them in school.

model appliances

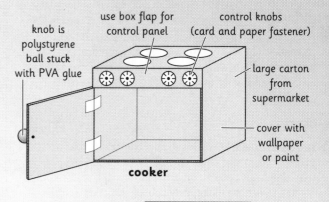

knob is polystyrene ball stuck with PVA glue

use box flap for control panel

control knobs (card and paper fastener)

large carton from supermarket

cover with wallpaper or paint

cooker

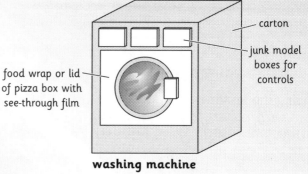

carton

junk model boxes for controls

food wrap or lid of pizza box with see-through film

washing machine

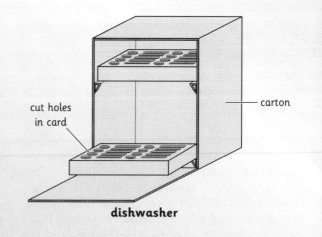

cut holes in card

carton

dishwasher

Teaching the lessons

Lesson 1 ①

Vocabulary

Electricity, flex, plug, point, switch

Introduction `10min`

Find out from the children what they understand by the word 'electric'. Write on the board the key words they use in their explanations.

Activities `25min`

Show the children one of the electrical points in the room. Warn them about the dangers of pushing anything into it or tampering with it in any way. Then show the children the parts of a point (no detail about circuits needs to be discussed but the dangers should be emphasized). Take the plug apart so that the children can see the wires inside it and that the wires are attached to the pins of the plug.

Divide the class into groups and ask the children to pass round the room-interior pictures and talk in their groups about where there might be electrical points in the rooms.

Closing the lesson `10min`

Bring the class together and ask the children about where there are electrical points in their homes. Warn the children again about the dangers.

Lesson 2 ②③

Vocabulary

Cooker, danger, electricity, hairdryer, kettle, refrigerator, safe, switch, washing machine; the names of other electrical appliances

Introduction `10min`

Ask the children to name some machines that need electricity to make them work. List them.

Activities `30min`

Divide the class into groups and give each group a stack of pictures of appliances which they can sort out in a variety of ways, including: type of appliance, room used in, and hand-held and non-hand-held.

Fix a picture of each kind of appliance to the board in turn and ask the children why we say that the appliance may be dangerous. In addition to the electrical dangers, they will be able to name heat, risk of scalding and naked flames as sources of danger. The dangers can be written up as annotations on the picture as shown above opposite.

Give each child a copy of **Copymaster 56** to complete, using the pictures on the board as clues for the work.

cooker switch —
– do not touch

hot plates burn

oven door handle – danger do not touch

never touch these – they control the heat

hot oven door can burn

Cooker

Closing the lesson `5min`

Quiz the children on the dangers in everyday machines.

Lesson 3 ④

Vocabulary

Burn, electric, electricity, flex, hot, off, on, plug, switch

Introduction `5min`

Tell the children that this is to be a words lesson in which they review all the words they now know about electricity. Ask them for some words to check that the ones they recall are in the card word list.

Activities `15min`

Show the children the model appliances and ask a volunteer to assign the card labels to the appropriate places on the appliance.

Closing the lesson `10min`

Remind the children of the care they should take with electrical points and machines and that they use what we call mains electricity.

After the lessons

Homework

With adult help, the children can survey their home to find out how many electrical points they have. They can also ask adults at home when they use electricity in the course of their work. **Copymaster 57** can be used to record the replies.

Investigations

The children could be accompanied round the school to spot all the ways in which electricity is used.

Assessment

For their own safety and that of others, the children all need to know the key facts from these lessons. They could be given an oral or picture test.

What does electricity make things do?

Learning targets

The children should be able to:

1 ➤➤ say that some devices use mains electricity while others use batteries
2 ➤➤ show that an electrical source is required to make these devices work
3 ➤➤ explore the idea that batteries need to be connected correctly to enable a device to work
4 ➤➤ say that electricity allows devices to do a variety of things, including heat up, emit light, move and emit sound

Before you start

Lesson preparation

Lesson 1

Set up a display involving pictures of mains electricity appliances and examples of battery-operated appliances. Some real appliances will need to be collected to be placed on the display. Photocopy Copymaster 58. Opposite is an example of a display.

Lesson 2

Access to some mains appliances which can be plugged in and turned on in the lesson will be needed. Examples might include a table lamp, hairdryer or electric toothbrush. Some battery-operated appliances will also be required so that the batteries can be taken out. These may include a radio, a torch and a remote-controlled toy car.

Lesson 3

The display used in Lesson 1 may be helpful here. Photocopy Copymaster 59. The children need access to battery-operated appliances, for example a torch, a remote-controlled toy, a walking toy, a radio, a hand-held computer game.

Investigations

You will need a collection of batteries of different sizes, including a watch or calculator battery and those commonly used in torches and radios.

Health and safety

Remind the children about the hazards of mains electricity and remember to point out that batteries should not be tampered with or opened.

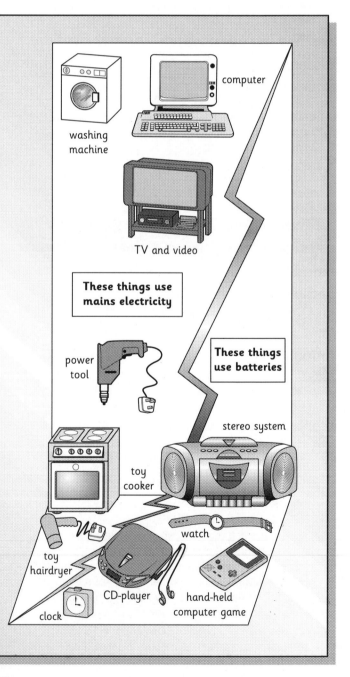

computer

washing machine

TV and video

These things use mains electricity

These things use batteries

power tool

stereo system

toy cooker

watch

toy hairdryer

CD-player

hand-held computer game

clock

Teaching the lessons

Lesson 1   ①

Vocabulary

Appliance, battery, device, electric, electricity, go, machine, mains, off, on, stop, switch

Introduction   [5 min]

Ask the children what they understand by 'mains-operated' and 'battery-operated'. Point out that things that need electricity to work are of two kinds. Some need to be plugged in to the mains, while others do not have an external lead and can often be carried around because they use the electricity that comes from batteries.

Activities   [20 min]

Draw the children's attention to the display and talk about the items in it. Take the cover off some of the battery-operated items so that the children can see the batteries.

Ask the children to complete a copy of **Copymaster 58**.

Closing the lesson   [5 min]

Call out a long list of appliances and see if the children can distinguish those that they think are mains-operated and those that are battery-operated. Here are some examples, including some which may be in the display. Mains-operated: CD-player, computer, drill, hairdryer, kettle, lamp, projector, refrigerator, television, toaster. Battery-operated: calculator, clock, hand-held computer game, radio, remote-controlled toy, toothbrush, torch, watch.

Lesson 2   ② ③

Vocabulary

Appliance, battery, device, electric, electricity, plug, power, source, switch

Introduction   [5 min]

Ask the children again what makes electrical appliances work. Demonstrate that they need electrical power to make them work.

Activities   [35 min]

Test the children's assertions by plugging in and switching on a lamp. Ask the children what is happening before it is plugged in, after you have plugged it in and when it is switched on. Follow the same procedure with the other mains equipment.

Divide the class into groups. Set up a piece of battery-operated equipment for each group. Lift off the battery cover. Allow the children in each group to have a good look at how the batteries are arranged.

Show the whole class the arrangement of batteries inside a battery-operated device. Replace the cover and show the children that the appliance works. Then remove the batteries and ask the children what will happen. Replace the cover and try to switch the

item on. Then replace the batteries in a different orientation and show the children that the equipment does not work (be careful as some electrical equipment can be damaged by reversing the current). Determine with the children that the device works with the batteries correctly arranged inside it.

Closing the lesson   [5 min]

Review what the children have learned during the lesson. Ask individuals to answer key questions.

Lesson 3   ④

Vocabulary

Give off, give out, heat, light, move, noise, sound, switch off, switch on; the names of the appliances on view in the classroom and in use during the lesson

Introduction   [5 min]

Show the children the classroom electric cooker or an electric heater and ask them what happens when it is switched on. Point out that the cooker or heater needs electricity to make it work. When they are switched on, they work by getting hot to cook our food or heat the room.

Activities   [30 min]

 Divide the class into groups. Give each group a battery-operated device and allow time for each child to switch it on and off. They can then agree about how the device works and what the electricity makes it do.

Invite each group to demonstrate their device and point out what happens when it is switched on.

Give each child a copy of **Copymaster 59** and ask them to draw pictures of appliances that get hot, make a noise, move around, and emit light.

Closing the lesson   [5 min]

Confirm what the children have recorded on Copymaster 59 and use appliances from the display to give more examples of what electricity can make happen.

After the lessons

Homework

Ask the children to list all the battery-operated devices they have in their homes.

Investigations

Set out a collection of batteries of varying sizes and ask the children to find out which kinds of appliances they come from. Talk about the idea that each device needs a power source to give the right amount of electricity for it to work.

Assessment

The children's oral and written work should enable you to ascertain the extent of their learning.

Making circuits

Learning targets

The children should be able to:

1 ➤ observe a circuit being made and broken

2 ➤ understand that a complete circuit is necessary for an electrical device to work

3 ➤ make a circuit with a lamp in it

4 ➤ make a circuit with a bell or buzzer in it

Before you start

Lesson preparation

Lesson 1

You will need suitable materials for making a circuit for the demonstration. These include circuit wire, crocodile clips, wire-cutters, a 1·5-volt battery and a lamp in a lamp holder. Photocopy Copymaster 60.

Lesson 2

Materials for making a circuit will be needed by each pair or group of children in the class. These include circuit wire, crocodile clips, a 1·5-volt battery and a lamp in a lamp holder.

Lesson 3

Materials for making a circuit will be needed by each pair or group of children in the class. These include circuit wire, crocodile clips, a 1·5-volt battery and a bell or buzzer. Photocopy Copymaster 61.

Investigations

Junk modelling materials and craft materials, including paper, card and paints are required for each pair or group of children carrying out the investigations. They will also need access to a box of circuit-making equipment, including at least the following: 1·5-volt batteries, bells, buzzers, circuit wire, crocodile clips, lamps in lamp holders, wire-cutters. They may also need switches. Photocopy Copymaster 62.

Health and safety

The children should take care with bare wire ends as they may be sharp. Warn them never to take a battery apart as there are harmful chemicals inside.

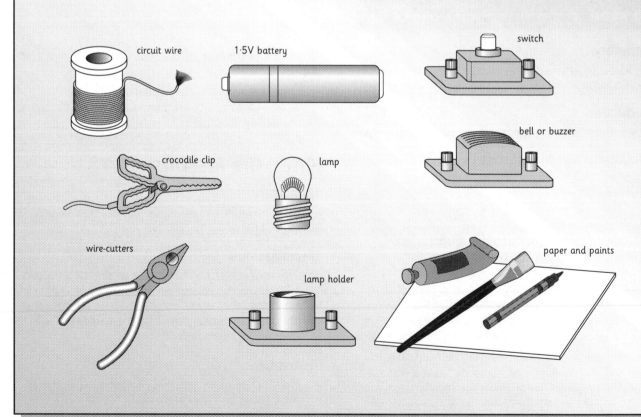

circuit wire   1·5V battery   switch

crocodile clip   lamp   bell or buzzer

wire-cutters   lamp holder   paper and paints

Teaching the lessons

Lesson 1 ① ②

Vocabulary

Battery, break, circuit, circuit wire, complete, crocodile clip, electricity, lamp, lamp holder, terminals

Introduction | 5 min

▦ Show the children the circuit-making equipment and give them all the new words they need to name the items.

Activities | 30 min

▦ While the children watch, make a circuit with a battery and a lamp in it (a switch can also be included in the circuit if you wish). Show the children that when all the wires are connected the circuit is complete and the lamp comes on. Disconnect the circuit, then connect it again at every point; in other words, at each battery terminal and at each lamp holder terminal (and at the switch terminal if there is one in the circuit). Point out to the children that when there is a break in the circuit, no matter where, the lamp does not come on and the circuit is said to be broken.

👤 Give each child a copy of **Copymaster 60** and invite them to draw the completed circuit and the broken circuit.

Closing the lesson | 10 min

▦ Ask one or two children to build the circuit while the others watch.

Lesson 2 ③

Vocabulary

Battery, break, circuit, circuit wire, complete, crocodile clip, electricity, lamp, lamp holder, terminals

Introduction | 5 min

▦ Check that the children understand that a circuit needs to be complete for electrical devices to work.

Activities | 30 min

👥 Divide the children into groups and give each group a box containing circuit-making equipment and ask them to allow each member of the group in turn to set up the circuit and get the lamp to light up. Visit each group to check that the connections are sound and the lamp is working.

▦ Ask each group in turn to show the class their circuit with the lamp lit up.

Closing the lesson | 5 min

▦ Review with the class the difficulties they may have had, the importance of good connections, the fragility of the lamp bulb, the need for a complete circuit and other particular points raised in the course of their work.

Lesson 3 ④

Vocabulary

Battery, bell, break, buzzer, circuit, circuit wire, complete, crocodile clip, electricity, terminals

Introduction | 5 min

▦ Show the children a bell, a buzzer or both. This may be a closed unit but the children can be shown the terminals.

Activities | 35 min

👥 Divide the class into groups. Give each group a box of circuit-making equipment and allow time for every child to make the circuit with a bell or buzzer in it.

👤 Give each child a copy of **Copymaster 61** to complete.

Closing the lesson | 5 min

▦ Review the work the children have done. If they have not put a switch in their circuit, introduce a switch to one of the circuits and demonstrate how it works.

After the lessons

Homework

Invite the children to use packaging, paper clips, paper fasteners and similar things to make a switch of their own. They can be brought into school and tested in a circuit in the classroom. Here is one suggestion for a switch but the children should be encouraged to design their own.

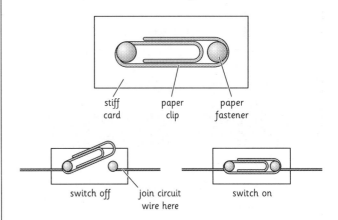

Investigations

Give the children some junk modelling materials and circuit-making equipment and invite them to make a model with a circuit in it. Examples are illustrated on **Copymaster 62**.

Assessment

Review your notes and observations on the children's work to establish their understanding of the idea of a complete circuit.

On the move

Learning targets

The children should be able to:

1 ➤➤ think about the ways they move

2 ➤➤ observe and describe movement around us

3 ➤➤ explore moving toys

Before you start

Lesson preparation

Lesson 1

The children will require access to the hall or playground for a PE lesson. This can be treated as a movement or dance lesson. If the children are very experienced in the use of apparatus this can be introduced. Mats, benches and other gym apparatus will then be required. Alternatively, small equipment, including balls and hoops may be required.

Lesson 2

Seek parental permission to take the children out of school for this lesson. Research a safe locality to take the children to observe movements. Extra adult help with supervision will also be required. Photocopy Copymaster 63.

Lesson 3

Assemble a collection of moving toys. These can include toys that the children propel, those operated by friction and clockwork, as well as battery-operated toys. Any toy that moves or invites movement is appropriate. Ask the children to bring toys to add to the display. Photocopy Copymaster 64.

Investigations

You will need video footage of animals and secondary sources containing information about natural phenomena like hurricanes, earthquakes and volcanoes.

Health and safety

As in all PE lessons and trips out of school, the children need to be reminded about their own safety and that of others.

Teaching the lessons

Lesson 1 ①

Vocabulary

Words associated with human movement, including bend, crawl, fast, lift, slide, slow, step, stretch, stride, turn, twist

Introduction [10min]

▦ Discuss with the children the kinds of movements humans can make. Write on the board the words they use.

Activities [30min]

▦ Take the children through a dance or PE lesson, giving, for example, the following instructions:

Find a space, limber up and stay on the spot.

Try moving your head, neck, upper body, lower body, arms, hands, fingers, knees.

Now move off the spot and move your legs and feet.

Try a different kind of movement.

Now try another.

Choose several children who have been moving well to demonstrate their sequences to the rest of the class.

Gather the children together and allow them to list the kinds of movement they have made. The children can then be asked to develop a moving-around sequence.

If mats, benches and other apparatus are available, half the session can include some of the floor work described above and the second half can include explorations of movement on the apparatus. If balls and other toys are to be used, these can be introduced for the second half of the session.

Closing the lesson [5min]

▦ Bring together the children's ideas about human movement. Point out that we need energy to move and that the energy to make our muscles work comes not from a battery but another energy store, namely, our food.

Lesson 2 ②

Vocabulary

All the words the children use in describing the movements they observe

Introduction 5min

In preparation for the children's trip outside, explain that they are going to be looking for all kinds of movement.

Activities 30min

Take the children to a safe locality where they can observe movements. They could watch, for example, a playgroup at play on big toys or a construction site from a safe distance.

Closing the lesson 15min

Using copies of **Copymaster 63**, if this is suitable, talk to the children about the kinds of movement they have seen.

Lesson 3 ③

Vocabulary

The names of all the toys on display; words for kinds of movement that the children describe

Introduction 10min

Use the class display to begin this lesson. Take things from the display and talk about the movements that can be made with them. Below is an example display.

Activities 30min

Divide the class into groups. Give each group several toys and ask the children to investigate the movements that can be made with them.

Invite each group to report back to the rest of the class about the kinds of movements their toys can make.

Give each child a copy of **Copymaster 64** and ask them to make a record of how a toy moves.

Closing the lesson 5min

Replace the toys on the display, talking about how they move.

After the lessons

Homework

Ask the children to find out if there is anyone in the family who regularly exercises, does aerobics or plays a sport. Perhaps they can talk to these people about the movements they make in their activities, the muscles they are using and the benefits they feel the activity provides.

Investigations

Also allow the children to view a video showing the movements of animals. Ask them to compile as long a list of movement words as they can.

Allow the children to research natural phenomena. Talk with the children about their findings about hurricanes, earthquakes and volcanoes. Discuss with them what is moving, how fast, where from and where to. (There is more opportunity to find out about winds in the Investigations for Topic 32 Push and pull).

Assessment

The children's levels of participation and concentration in the lessons, along with their contributions to the vocabulary lists should indicate how well they have focused on movement.

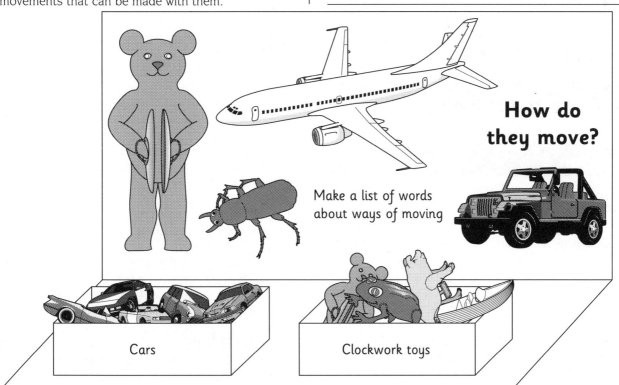

How do they move?

Make a list of words about ways of moving

Cars

Clockwork toys

Push and pull

Learning targets

The children should be able to:

1 ➡➡ explore what starts things moving
2 ➡➡ understand that something happens to make things stop moving
3 ➡➡ explore push and pull forces

Before you start

Lesson preparation

Lesson 1

The children will need access to all parts of the classroom and possibly to other parts of the school. Two or more glove puppets and equipment and toys from around the classroom are also needed. Photocopy Copymaster 65.

Lesson 2

A water tray with some water toys would be helpful here. Also, erect a simple washing line outside on which some clothes can be hung. The children should also be allowed to look out of the windows to watch trees and other objects in the wind. Alternatively, they can be taken outside to make their observations.

Lesson 3

A child's bicycle would be an invaluable resource here. Alternatively, a large picture of a child's bicycle is needed. Several copies of cards with the words 'push' and 'pull' on them will be required. Photocopy Copymaster 66.

Investigations

The equipment here will depend on the exact nature of the investigations that the children wish to undertake. The sort of things that may be helpful could include books about the wind and other natural forces, materials suitable for making a windsock (for example, lightweight material, wire and canes, along with suitable adhesive), toy waterwheels, jugs and water trays, toy sand-wheels, scoops and sand trays, timers and measuring cylinders.

Health and safety

The children need to be reminded about being careful.

Teaching the lessons

Lesson 1 ① ② ③

Vocabulary

Force, move, pull, push, start, stop

Introduction [5 min]

By miming movements in front of the children, introduce them to the words in the vocabulary list. Place special emphasis on the word 'force' and point out that without what scientists call 'force' nothing would ever move.

Activities [30 min]

Using two glove puppets, demonstrate push and pull. For example, the puppets can have a tug-of-war, a tussle, push a book or a toy car, open drawers and doors, lids and pens. After a short demonstration in which the characters of the puppets are set up, the children can work the puppets while others offer a commentary on the pushing and pulling going on.

Divide the class into groups. Ask each group to take a sheet of paper and record, as a group, two columns of data. The first column can be headed 'push' and the second one 'pull'. The children should list as many things as they can see or find in the classroom, library or craft area, where these forces occur.

Following the group work, the children can make their own individual record on **Copymaster 65**.

Closing the lesson [5 min]

Review the group examples of push and pull around the room, demonstrating the pushes and pulls. The puppets can be used again if this is appropriate.

Lesson 2 ③

Vocabulary

Air, force, move, pull, push, start, stop, water

Introduction | 5min |

Remind the children of push and pull forces. Ask them what else they can think of that pushes and pulls, apart from us using our muscles. They may, for example, talk about other animals or machines.

Activities | 30min |

Ask the children to look through the window and talk about the push and pull of moving air. Alternatively, take them outside to inspect the washing on the line. If it is appropriate, talk about the changing force of the wind and the expected rate of drying. Ask the children what a strong wind does to the trees, themselves, flags, litter and the sails on a boat.

Show the children the action of a toy waterwheel and discuss what the force of the water is doing. Ask key questions, for example:

How does a waterwheel work?

Does the wheel move faster if more water is poured on to it?

Where is the push and the pull?

Write on the board the words they use in their responses. Allow individual children to try out some of their own suggestions while the rest of the class watch.

Closing the lesson | 5min |

Review the force of wind and water from the children's own experiences.

Lesson 3 ① ② ③

Vocabulary

Force, move, pull, push, start, stop; the names of bicycle parts mentioned by the children, including brakes, pedals, wheels

Introduction | 15min |

With the children, examine the bicycle or picture of a bicycle and talk to them about its parts. Then invite them to say where the push and pull are at work when we are riding a bicycle. Here are some examples: pedals, gears, brake pads, whole bicycle when it is not being ridden, brake levers.

Activities | 10min |

Give every child a copy of **Copymaster 66** so that they can indicate on the picture some of the push and pull examples.

Closing the lesson | 15min |

Invite all the children to watch while you set up a drama involving a child on a bicycle. This should involve push and pull and can be used as an opportunity to talk about cycling safely.

After the lessons

Homework

Ask the children to make a storyboard of themselves pushing and pulling to arrive at school in the morning. The storyboard may look something like this:

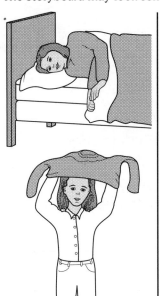

I wake up and **push** off the bedclothes

I **pull** on my sweater

I **push** the milk jug towards my brother while having breakfast

Investigations

Allow the children to make studies of the following questions.

What is wind force?

How is the wind measured?

Can we make a windsock?

Where is the push and the pull?

How much sand is needed to make a toy sand-wheel go?

What happens when twice as much sand is poured on – does it go twice as fast?

Where is the push and the pull?

Invite the children to examine large school playground equipment outside or in pictures to make statements about when there is push and pull on these.

Assessment

Look at the children's work on Copymasters 65 and 66 and their contributions to group work.

Speeding up, slowing down or changing direction

Learning targets

The children should be able to:

1 ➤➤ explore what makes things speed up
2 ➤➤ explore what makes things slow down
3 ➤➤ look at and describe changes in direction

Before you start

Lesson preparation

Lesson 1

Set up a Scalextric® track before the lesson. Collect the following: a small toy car for every child in the class, and balsa or other wood planks and blocks.

Lesson 2

Obtain video footage of a football match, go-kart race or both. Photocopy Copymaster 67.

Lesson 3

Collect a small bag of marbles for each pair of children. The children need access to space to play with the marbles. Photocopy Copymaster 68.

Investigations

Small balls will be required. Also record video footage of part of a snooker or bowls match.

Health and safety

Remind the children to take care of equipment and be mindful of the safety of themselves and others.

Teaching the lessons

Lesson 1 ① ② ③

Vocabulary

Change direction, force, going faster, going slower, hand-held cars, obstruction, ramp, slow down, speed up

Introduction 〔10min〕

▦ Show the children the Scalextric® in action. Ask them to comment on the force making the cars go, whether they actually go faster and, if so, why this happens. Ask them to suggest ways of slowing down the cars.

Activities 〔25min〕

◆ Divide the class into groups. Allow each group to have access to toy cars and equipment to make a run or ramp. Ask the children to experiment to try to answer some of the following questions:

Which car goes fastest on the flat? Why?

Does a car go faster if it is pushed harder?

Do smaller cars travel faster than bigger cars?

Does every car travel the same distance if started from the top of a ramp? Why not?

▦ Bring the children together and ask them to raise some more questions that are puzzling them and about the phenomena they have seen.

Closing the lesson 〔10min〕

▦ Bring together some of the observations the children have made.

Lesson 2 ① ② ③

Vocabulary

Change direction, force, slow down, speed up

Introduction 〔5min〕

▦ Remind the children that a force is required not only to start things moving but also to make them speed up, slow down, stop or change direction.

Activities 25min

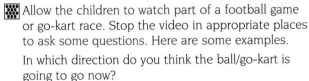 Allow the children to watch part of a football game or go-kart race. Stop the video in appropriate places to ask some questions. Here are some examples.

In which direction do you think the ball/go-kart is going to go now?

Where does the player want the ball to go?

What change of direction must the driver take?

How does it feel when your Mum or Dad turns a corner sharply in the car?

What happens when you are in a car or bus that stops sharply?

Give each child a copy of **Copymaster 67** and invite them to complete it. This is about football; an alternative copymaster will be needed if you want the children to work exclusively on go-karting.

Closing the lesson 5min

Inspect some of the completed copymasters and discuss the answers with the children.

Lesson 3 ① ② ③

Vocabulary

Change direction, force, slow down, speed up

Introduction 5min

Collect a small bag of marbles for each pair of children. The children need access to the hall or playground for part of the lesson.

Activities 35min

Allow the children the chance to share the marbles, then play a short game in pairs. Ask them especially to look at what happens when the marbles strike one another.

Discuss their findings with the children and give them further challenges, for example:

What difference does it make if one marble is rolled much harder than the other?

How can you make a marble hit another and then go in the direction you want it to?

Does the size of a marble affect its speed or direction?

Give the children another opportunity to work with the marbles.

The children can record on **Copymaster 68** some of the things they found out.

Closing the lesson 5min

Point out to the children that the marbles required the children's push force to start them moving and show them how the change of direction alters depending on the angle of impact.

After the lessons

Homework

Invite the children to watch a ball game and look out for evidence of forces at work.

Investigations

Give the children the opportunity to work with small balls, either individually or in pairs, to see how they can predict the direction and speed of a ball which they start to move.

Invite the children to watch video footage of part of a snooker or bowls match. Allow them to talk about what happens when one ball strikes another or in snooker when a ball hits the side of the table.

Assessment

Observe the children's involvement in the lessons and their contributions to discussions.

Road safety

Learning targets

The children should be able to:

1 ➡➡ talk about road safety
2 ➡➡ to cross the road safely
3 ➡➡ identify some of the forces affecting our safety

Before you start

Lesson preparation

Lesson 1

Obtain safety video material if possible and posters and leaflets about road safety. A street play mat with a street scene and small cars and road signs to fit on the play mat are all needed. Photocopy Copymaster 69.

Lesson 2

Seek parental permission to take the children out of school. Recruit extra adults to help you supervise them. Make a crossing patrol lollipop and borrow or make a crossing patrol costume suitable for a child. If possible, ask the crossing patrol person who is attached to your school to come to the lesson and talk to the children for a few minutes.

Lesson 3

Space in which the children can act out a drama is needed. Photocopy Copymaster 70.

Investigations

According to the investigations undertaken by the children, they will need access to the following: streets in the vicinity of the school (accompanied by an adult), clipboards, large sheets of paper and card and art materials for making posters, as well as leaflets about road safety from a range of sources.

Health and safety

This entire topic is focused on the safety of the children.

Teaching the lessons

Lesson 1 ①

Vocabulary

Brake, force, kerb drill, listen, look, pedestrian crossing, pelican crossing, safety, speed, stopping time, think, traffic lights, zebra crossing

Introduction 5min

▦ Explain to the children that they will be talking about road safety. Allow them to share their experiences of risks, hazards and dangers in connection with roads.

Activities 30min

▦ Invite the children to watch and discuss relevant footage from a safety video if this is available.

▦ Using the play mat, set up three or four situations where a child, either alone or in the company of an adult, wants to cross the road. Talk through what they should do to cross safely.

▦ Divide the class into groups. Give each child a copy of **Copymaster 69**. Allow them in their groups to read the statements listed on it and to talk amongst themselves about the statements.

Closing the lesson 10min

▦ Take each statement in turn on Copymaster 69 and discuss its validity with the children.

Lesson 2 ②

Vocabulary

Brake, force, listen, look, kerb drill, lollipop, pedestrian crossing, pelican crossing, safety, speed, think, stopping time, traffic lights, zebra crossing

Introduction 10min

▦ Draw two chalk lines on the classroom floor or the playground to represent the edges of a road. Invite volunteers to act as though they are crossing the road. Check that they go through the appropriate sequence of actions before deciding that it is safe to cross. Then allow a child to don the crossing patrol costume and guide the children across the road.

Activities `20min`

 Take the children out of school and with the help of additional adults, allow them to practise crossing the road safely. Stress the hazards that moving and parked vehicles pose.

Closing the lesson `10min`

Bring the children back into the classroom. If the crossing patrol person is available, they can remind the children about the road hazards. If the patrol person cannot come to the class, review with the children what they have learned in the lesson.

Lesson 3 ① ② ③

Vocabulary

Brake, force, listen, look, kerb drill, lollipop, pedestrian crossing, pelican crossing, safety, speed, think, stopping time, traffic lights, zebra crossing

Introduction `5min`

Remind the children of the key points covered in Lessons 1 and 2.

Activities `30min`

Divide the class into groups. Ask each group to create a little drama involving traffic and crossing a road. Visit all the groups and advise them about content including the safety points they know.

Allow each group to perform their drama to the rest of the class.

Give every child a copy of **Copymaster 70**. Allow them a few minutes to read it through. Then take

each statement in turn and discuss it with the children.

Closing the lesson `5min`

Review the reasons why we need to take care when crossing the road.

After the lessons

Homework

Ask the children to create a booklet giving the points to remember when crossing the road. They could also be invited to invent a road safety board game. Below is an example which could be shown to them.

Investigations

Allow the children to survey the safest places to cross roads in the vicinity of the school.

Invite the children to create a road safety poster which will catch the eye of children their age.

Together with the children, compare all the road safety advice available from official sources including the police, the Royal Society for the Prevention of Accidents, and County Council Road Safety Units.

Assessment

Children will have made physical and verbal contributions to the classes, which should serve to show the extent of their understanding.

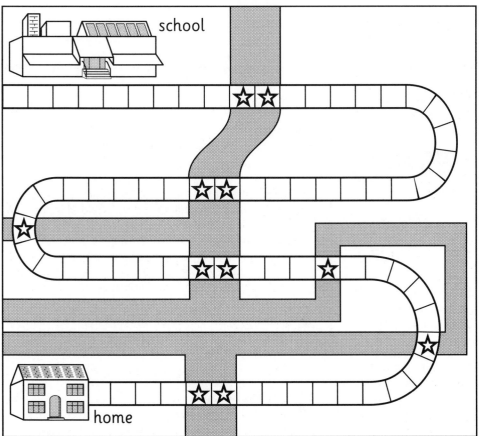

A simple track game for two players.
Go from school to home.
Throw a dice to move.
Draw in roads (here shaded).
When a player lands on a point where a road is crossed ☆, the player explains how to cross safely. Safety rules are on a crib card for the other player to check.

Light toys

Learning targets

The children should be able to:

1 ➤➤ explore light effects by looking
2 ➤➤ explore light and reflective surfaces
3 ➤➤ think about how light toys work

Before you start

Lesson preparation

Lesson 1

You will need a wide range of junk materials for the light experiments. Here are some suggestions: card cores from kitchen rolls, cellophane sweet-wrappers in a wide variety of colours, pieces of card, each with a single hole varying in size from a pinhole to one the size of a 5p piece. Photocopy Copymaster 71.

Lesson 2

The following will be needed: enough plane safety mirrors to allow each child in the class to have one, aluminium foil including take-away food trays and lids, spoons and other kitchen items which reflect light. Photocopy Copymaster 72.

Lesson 3

Set up a display of toys which use light to work, including, for example, kaleidoscopes, a model theatre and Lights Alive®.

Investigations

Resources needed here will depend on the investigations undertaken by the children but could include the following: a bicycle reflector, colour filters, posters and photographs showing road signs, reflective materials, reflective safety armbands and torches.

Health and safety

Warn the children against shining lights into one another's eyes.

Teaching the lessons

Lesson 1 ①

Vocabulary

Black, blue, green, light, look, red, see, white, yellow; other colour words used by the children

Introduction ⬚ 10 min

Look through a cardboard tube and voice your thoughts, for example, 'I can see around me', 'I can look at what is far away and what is close to me', 'I cannot see what is in the dark corner of the stock cupboard'. Then try looking through coloured cellophane and again say aloud what you can see. For example, when looking through purple cellophane, 'The door looks blue', 'This yellow book looks greenish'. Use the holed pieces of card and try looking through the holes. Ask the children to investigate and comment on what they can see through the holes.

Activities ⬚ 25 min

👥 Ask the children to pair up. Allow the pairs to repeat the activities that you showed them in the introduction. They are using light to see and it is important that they focus on this. They should use everyday words to talk about their field of vision, the colour effects and the fact that they can see through a very small hole as well as through a larger one (this will be useful in understanding how cameras and the eye work at Key Stage 2). Note that even if resources are shared, every child should experience looking through the holes in the cards.

👤 Give each child a copy of **Copymaster 71** and allow them to complete it, repeating what they did in the previous activity if necessary.

Closing the lesson ⬚ 10 min

Discuss with the children some of the observations they made and the colour effects they have seen.

Lesson 2 (2)

Vocabulary

Mirror, reflection, shiny

Introduction | 5min

Demonstrate to the children that some of the items they will be using are shiny and reflect light. If the sun is shining, sunlight can be reflected by a shiny object on to a wall or other surface in the classroom, demonstrating various patterns and effects caused by reflection.

Activities | 40min

Give each child in the class a plane safety mirror or alternative reflective surface and allow them time to explore reflections.

Bring the class together and give the children the chance to discuss their experiences.

Ask the children to work in pairs and talk about what they are doing. Set them challenges, such as, for example:

Can you reflect light from a non-reflective surface on to another non-reflective surface?

What happens when you cover a reflective surface so that light does not reach it?

Do the surfaces reflect light equally well in the darkest corner of the room as in the brightest part of the room?

Give each child a copy of **Copymaster 72** and ask them to write about their experiments.

Closing the lesson | 5min

Review the work the children have done, checking that they understand that light does not emanate from reflective surfaces but that it comes from another source and is reflected off these surfaces.

Lesson 3 (3)

Vocabulary

Electric, light, reflect, switch, toy; colour words used by the children

Introduction | 10min

Draw the children's attention to the display of light toys. Below is an example of a display.

Activities | 30min

Divide the class into groups. Give each group a light toy and allow time for every child in the group to experiment with the toy.

Ask each group in turn to talk about their toy, how it works and the light effects it produces. Add to the children's explanations where necessary.

Ask the groups to swap toys and repeat the experiments.

Closing the lesson | 5min

Summarize the light effects produced with the toys. If it is appropriate, mention that we call something that emanates light a light source (*see* Topic 38).

After the lessons

Homework

Ask the children to draw a picture showing some of the ways we use reflected light.

Investigations

Give the children a range of materials (for example, about fifteen samples) and ask them to rank them according to how well they reflect light.

Allow the children to try out colour filters and shine torchlight through them. The filters can be superimposed on one another to achieve different light effects.

Ask the children whether they can think of important ways in which we use reflected light, for example, reflectors on the back of bicycles, safety armbands, safety waistcoats for road and railway workers, and reflectors on road signs and barriers.

Assessment

Look carefully at the work the children have done on Copymasters 71 and 72 and assess their contributions to group and whole-class work.

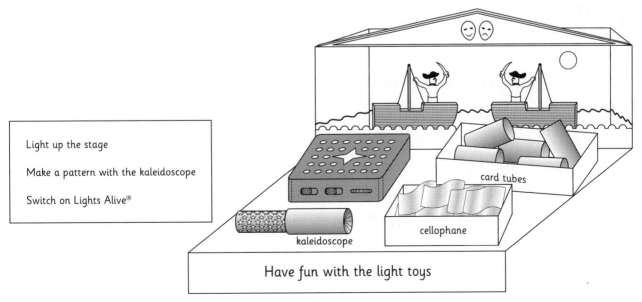

Light up the stage

Make a pattern with the kaleidoscope

Switch on Lights Alive®

kaleidoscope

card tubes

cellophane

Have fun with the light toys

Light and darkness

Learning targets

The children should be able to:

1 ➤➤ explore light and shadow effects using a torch
2 ➤➤ identify some nocturnal animals
3 ➤➤ see the different lighting effects achieved by lighting something from different directions

Before you start

Lesson preparation

Lesson 1

Every child needs a torch for this lesson. They will also need access to a room where the light levels can be reduced using curtains or blinds. Create a list of 'torch challenges' which can be mounted on the wall. Some suggestions appear in the lesson notes below.

Lesson 2

Borrow a short film or some video footage showing nocturnal creatures. Books, CD-ROMs and other sources of information about such animals are also important here. Photocopy Copymaster 73.

Lesson 3

A room with blackout facilities is required, along with a powerful torch. Photocopy Copymaster 74.

Investigations

Small pieces of transparent plastic sheeting are required.

Health and safety

Warn the children against the temptation to shine torchlight into one another's eyes.

Teaching the lessons

Lesson 1   ①

Vocabulary

Beam, darkness, light, look, see, shine, torch

Introduction   5 min

▦ Show the children a torch and explain that you would like them to experiment with it during the lesson. Show them the list of torch challenges, to which the children can add their own.

Here are some examples:

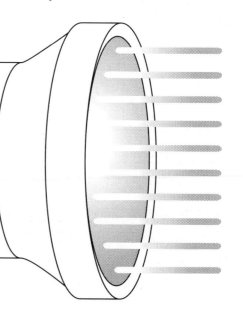

Torch challenges
* Shine it at a light. * Shine it in the dark.
* Put a hand in front of it. Talk about the
    shadows made. * Shine it through fabric.
* Make a dancing light pattern.
* Compare torches for brightness.

Activities `25 min`

👤 Allow the children a few minutes to operate the torches, then gradually reduce the light levels in the room so that the children can see the effects.

▦ Switch on the lights, switch off all the torches and let the children discuss the effects they observed. These may include observations such as, for example, 'Brighter light helped me see better', 'I could not see in the dark except by torchlight'. If there is time, allow the children to return to their experimentation.

Closing the lesson `10 min`

▦ Using a torch demonstrate the following ideas: we need light to see, some lights are brighter than others, and we can observe shadows when a light is shone on an object.

Lesson 2 ②

Vocabulary

Badger, bushbaby, dark, fox, gerbil, hamster, jaguar, lion, long-eared owl, night, nightjar, nocturnal, possum, see; the names of other animals that are predominantly nocturnal

Introduction `5 min`

▦ Discuss with the children the idea that on the whole humans rest when it is dark. Point out that some people are needed to work at night and need street lighting, car headlamps and lighting in their workplaces in order to see. Tell the children that some animals have very sensitive sight and other senses that allow them to move around safely in darkness.

Activities `30 min`

▦ Show the children the film or video footage of nocturnal animals.

▣▣ Divide the class into groups. Share the other resources among the work groups and allow the children time to find out what they can about these creatures.

👤 Give each child a copy of **Copymaster 73**. Identify the creatures shown on it. Talk about additional information concerning their behaviour, which may have emerged during earlier activities. If children in the class have pet hamsters or gerbils, they can report on their levels of activity at night.

Closing the lesson `5 min`

▦ Show the children the best part of the film or video again.

Lesson 3 ③

Vocabulary

Above, beam, below, darkness, effects, in front, light, to one side, stage lighting, torch

Introduction `5 min`

▦ This lesson provides another opportunity to introduce the children to a discussion of light, dark and shadows. Ask the children what they understand by the word 'shadow'. Accept answers like 'where the light does not go' and 'behind something that is lit at the front'.

Activities `30 min`

▦ Black out the room and ask a volunteer to sit in a chair so that all the other children can see them. Hold a lit torch under the face of the volunteer and point out where the light and dark parts of the face are. Discuss the kind of appearance it gives to the face. Then light the head from above and from the front in turn, looking at the shadows and general overall appearance each time. Point out that stage lighting uses direction as well as colour to change the appearance of performers.

👤 Give each child a copy of **Copymaster 74** and allow them to use a pencil to indicate the shadows.

Closing the lesson `5 min`

▦ Discuss the children's experiences of the theatre or stage shows and some of the light effects that they may have seen.

After the lessons

Homework

Invite the children to play with a torch at home with parental permission. They can report their experiences to the class.

Investigations

Offer the children a small piece of sheet plastic and ask them to determine under what circumstances they can see through it. They might say, for example, that they can see through it if there is light both sides or if they shine a light through it. Alternatively, they might say that they cannot see through it if there is no light on the other side or if they are in total darkness.

Assessment

The children's involvement in practical activities should give most evidence of their learning.

Shadow play

Learning targets

The children should be able to:

1 ➤➤ explore making shadows in sunlight

2 ➤➤ explore making shadows using a torch

3 ➤➤ recognize that the shape of a shadow can change

Before you start

Lesson preparation

Lesson 1

Choose a sunny day and allow the children access to the playground. It may be appropriate for the children to change into their PE kit first. Take some large sticks of playground chalk with you.

Lesson 2

Every child will need a torch for this lesson. They will also need access to a room where the light levels can be reduced using curtains or blinds. Photocopy Copymaster 75.

Lesson 3

An overhead projector, light box or similar equipment which projects a strong beam of light, and a white screen would be useful here.

Photocopy Copymaster 76. Before the lesson, prepare some photographs of shadows of familiar objects from usual and unusual angles that can be cast on to a screen, or some silhouettes depicting shadow shapes. Some examples are shown below.

Investigations

A sunny day is required and the children should be accompanied outside the school building. Photocopy Copymaster 77.

Health and safety

Warn the children never to look directly at the sun, even when wearing sunglasses, as this can damage their eyes.

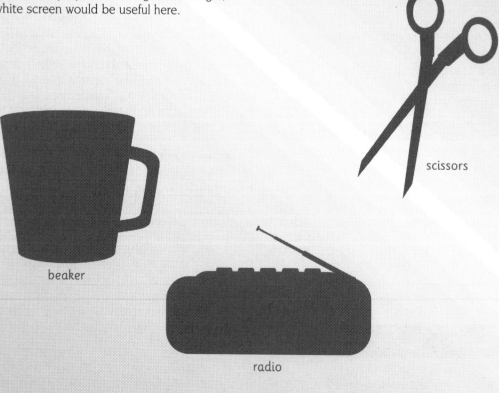

scissors

beaker

radio

Teaching the lessons

Lesson 1 ①

Vocabulary

Dark, light, movement, shadow, sun, sunshine

Introduction [10 min]

Tell the children that they are going to be looking at and creating shadows during this lesson. Use a checklist of key words to help the class read the vocabulary they are going to need.

Activities [40 min]

Take the children outside and using one or two volunteers, point out their shadows. Move the volunteers around, offering suggestions and challenges, such as, for example:

Where is the sun?

Where is the shadow?

What will happen to the shadow if one of you stands with their back to the sun?

What will happen to the shadow if one of you stands with their side to the sun?

What happens to the shadow when the sun goes behind a cloud?

Place the children in pairs and invite them to make shadows that fit together. They can, for example, make shadows that show a pair of people talking, shaking hands or dancing. Then they can create some shadows that look like mythical creatures.

Bring the class together and ask some pairs to demonstrate their shadows. These can be drawn round on the playground with classroom chalk.

Closing the lesson [5 min]

Review with the children the fact that shadows occur when the sun shines on something. When the sun is obscured, the shadow fades and may not be visible at all.

Lesson 2 ②

Vocabulary

Level, light source, screen, shadow

Introduction [5 min]

This lesson gives the children a chance to revisit some of the work they did in Topic 36. Tell the children that the focus here is different from the earlier lesson. Here, the children's area of interest is the shadows being made.

Activities [30 min]

Lower the light levels so that distinct shadows can be produced. Allow the children to make shadows on a light-coloured wall or a screen.

Give each child a copy of **Copymaster 75** so that they can write and draw some of their work on shadows.

Gradually raise the general level of light in the classroom, then lower it again so the children can observe the effect on the shadows they are producing.

Closing the lesson [5 min]

This has been another exploratory lesson. There may be children who observe that the object casting a shadow is between the light source and the wall or screen.

Lesson 3 ③

Vocabulary

Light, object, shadow

Introduction [10 min]

Use the projector or light box to produce a light beam big enough for all the children to see. Place some common objects in the beam and ask the children to examine the shadows. These could include, for example, a table fork, a mug, a paper doily, a book and a clear plastic ruler.

Activities [25 min]

Now vary the orientation of the objects in the beam of light so that the shadows change shape.

Place the pictures or silhouettes round the room and give each child a copy of **Copymaster 76**. Ask them to draw the object that belongs to each shadow.

Closing the lesson [10 min]

Review the children's drawings, discussing their answers. Allow one or two children to stand in the light beam so that a silhouette of their face can be seen.

After the lessons

Homework

Ask the children to see if they can spot a shadow in their house. They can record what it is a shadow of on **Copymaster 77**, if this is appropriate. They can then draw round it on newspaper and these can be compared and displayed in the classroom.

Investigations

Invite the children to walk round the edge of the shadow produced by a school building or a piece of large playground apparatus. Ask them to draw the building or apparatus and its shadow.

Assessment

Use the children's oral and written contributions to establish what they have learned.

PHYSICAL PROCESSES

TOPIC **38**

Light sources

Learning targets

The children should be able to:

1 ➤➤ see that light comes from a variety of sources
2 ➤➤ recognize that shiny things are not sources of light
3 ➤➤ say something about light sources used in the past
4 ➤➤ name some ways we use lights
5 ➤➤ say something about the special need for light in some jobs

Before you start

Lesson preparation

Lesson 1

The children need access to a range of sources of light in this lesson. These can include a torch, sunshine, a table lamp and a street lamp. If the weather is not sunny, a poster showing the sun would be useful. Some objects with shiny surfaces would be useful too, for example, a foil lid from a food container and some kitchen utensils.

Lesson 2

You will need books, CD-ROMs and other sources of information about lighting used in the past. A candle in a candle-holder, a safe surface on which to stand the candle, an oil lamp if one is available, or pictures of lamps used in the past would also be helpful. You could also include lamps from other cultures. Photocopy Copymaster 78.

Lesson 3

Create a class display like the one shown in the lesson notes below. It could be assembled as the lesson progresses. Alternatively, it can be completed before the lesson and you can reveal it to the children after they have discussed the topic. The children will also need access to places round the school. A set of fairy lights would be useful. Gather resources showing pictures of a range of people at work. Photocopy Copymaster 79.

Investigations

Ask the children to investigate in detail a light source or lamp used in the past to find out how it worked, where it was used and by whom.

Health and safety

Take care not to allow children near naked candle flames. Warn them of the danger of matches and make sure that they are not left in the classroom.

Teaching the lessons

Lesson 1 ➊ ➋

Vocabulary

Battery, electric lamp, electricity, light source, street lamp, sun, sunshine, torch; other words the children use

Introduction (10 min)

Talk to the children about where we get light from. How many things can they name? List them on the board. Group similar kinds of light source. For example, a bedside lamp may go with a desk lamp, fairy lights may go with lights in a shop window. Tell the children that the place from which light emanates is called a source and that all the light we have on Earth ultimately comes from the sun (the only exception is the light obtained from atomic processes but the children do not need to know this at this phase of their education).

Activities (30 min)

- Demonstrate some of the light sources to the children and show them pictures of those that are not available. These can include a torch, sunshine or a poster showing the sun, a table lamp and a street lamp.
- Divide the class into groups. Give each group examples of shiny surfaces and a light source. Ask the children to look at and experiment with both.
- Bring the children together and establish that the shiny things merely reflect light from a source; they are not light sources themselves. Ask them how this can be confirmed. Check that they understand that if no source of light is near a shiny object, the object does not reflect and is no longer shiny.

Closing the lesson (5 min)

- Check that the children understand what a light source is.

Lesson 2 ③

Vocabulary

Candle, flame, lamp, light, oil, source, wick

Introduction 15min

Talk about the light sources available to people in a variety of cultures over the centuries. Use pictures to show what people used. Light a candle in a candle-holder set on a safe surface and talk to the children about the advantages and disadvantages of such a form of lighting. If possible, the room can be blacked out so that the children can see how restricted the light from one candle is.

Activities 35min

Using appropriate resources, ask the children to create a group picture of a form of lighting from the past and find out how it worked.

Allow the child time to write some of what they have learned on a copy of **Copymaster 78**.

Closing the lesson 5min

Remind the children that all our energy, including light energy, ultimately comes from the sun.

Lesson 3 ④ ⑤

Vocabulary

Darkness, lights, security, seeing, signal, use, warning; other words the children use

Introduction 10min

Ask the children to name some of the ways we use lights. As they offer suggestions, set up the display of light uses or reveal pictures from the display as they arise in the discussion. Reveal the display in its entirety when the children have given all their suggestions. Plug in and switch on the fairy lights to remind the children that we sometimes use them for decoration. An example display is shown below.

Activities 30min

Take the children round the school to see how many different uses of lights they can spot.

Talk about the kinds of lights people use in their jobs. The children may have parents who use lamps in special ways. Give each child a copy of **Copymaster 79** to assist the discussion.

Allow the children to complete Copymaster 79.

Closing the lesson 5min

Help the children to sum up orally the uses of lights and some special occupational uses.

After the lessons

Homework

Ask the children to get information from their Mum or Dad about the light sources they use in the course of a day. For example:

Action	Source
Wake up with daylight	Sun
Press light on clock to see time clearly	Battery
Put on light in kitchen	Mains electricity

Investigations

Invite the children to find out the answers to some of these questions (answers need not go beyond a simple explanation at this phase of children's education):

What is put into street lamps to make them work?

What do the lamps in car headlamps look like?

What is a 'strip' or fluorescent light?

Assessment

Look at the children's written work as well as their contributions to the discussions.

What do we use lights for?

For security

To warn

To show that something is switched on

To see in the dark

As a signal – police

The sun, the Earth and the moon

Learning targets

The children should know:

1 ➡➡ some facts about the sun
2 ➡➡ some facts about planet Earth
3 ➡➡ some facts about the moon

Before you start

Lesson preparation

Lesson 1

Books, CD-ROMs and other sources about the sun for a young audience are required here. Also collect together some beachwear including a swimsuit, a tee shirt, sunglasses and a high-factor sun cream. Photocopy Copymaster 80.

Lesson 2

A globe and books, CD-ROMs and other sources of information about planet Earth are needed here. Photocopy Copymaster 81.

Lesson 3

Books, CD-ROMs and other sources of information about the moon are needed. Borrow some video footage of the moon for the children to watch. Make a chart showing the shape of the moon in its different phases. This does not need to be a fully detailed sequence but is merely to draw the children's attention to the 'shapes of moon' which they may have seen.

Investigations

Books, CD-ROMs and other sources of information about the solar system for a young audience are required.

Health and safety

Warn the children in the strongest possible terms that they must on no account look directly at the sun.

Teaching the lessons

Lesson 1 ①

Vocabulary

Burn, heat, light, orbit, solar system, star, sun

Introduction | 10 min |

▨ Ask the children what they know about the sun. Write the key words they use on the board and correct any misunderstandings. Introduce the children to the information sources, showing them how to access the facts they need.

Activities | 40 min |

♣ Divide the class into groups. Give each group one of the resource books, allowing one group of two or three children access to the CD-ROM, if possible. Ask them to read out together four facts about the sun.

▨ Bring the children together and ask them to call out the facts they found. Write or draw on the board to help them to remember these.

▨ Show the children the swimsuit and a tee shirt, sunglasses and a high-factor sun cream. Point out the danger of looking directly at the sun (even when wearing sunglasses, as they do not offer enough protection). Discuss the hazards involved in exposing naked skin to the sun.

👤 Allow the children time to write something about what they have learned on **Copymaster 80**.

Closing the lesson | 5 min |

▨ Review the facts the children now know about the sun, confirming that the sun is a star, that the Earth goes round it and that the sun is the source of heat and light on Earth.

Lesson 2 ②

Vocabulary

Air, Earth, land, ocean, orbit, planet, solar system

Introduction | 10 min |

▨ Ask the children what they know about the Earth.

Draw a giant circle on the board and write what they know inside it. This may include things like: we live on it, it is like a ball, it is in space and animals live here too.

Activities [35min]

■ Show the globe to the children. Point out the United Kingdom. Show the children that most of the Earth is ocean and that the dark parts show the land.

■ Allow the children time to begin writing on **Copymaster 81**.

■ Call the class together and, using the available resources, show them the pictures and read out the important facts.

■ Give the children a chance to add to the work they have done on Copymaster 81.

Closing the lesson [5min]

■ Ask each child in turn to say one thing they have learned in this lesson and see how long a list of facts can be produced.

Lesson 3 ③

Vocabulary

Moon, night, satellite, shape

Introduction [10min]

■ Tell the children that the moon is a satellite of the Earth and that it is much smaller than the Earth. Talk about when the children have seen the moon. Point out that, unlike the sun, the moon does not give out light but reflects the sun's light so that we can see it. The moon can be seen during the day.

Activities [20min]

■ Allow the children to watch the video footage of the moon and comment on it.

■ Ask the children to draw their own pictures of the moon.

Closing the lesson [10min]

■ Draw the children's attention to the chart showing 'moon shapes' and remind them that the moon is broadly spherical but we cannot always see all of it. If it is appropriate, mention that we only ever see one side of the moon. Below is a sample chart.

After the lessons

Homework

Ask the children to see if anyone in their family remembers watching astronauts in space. The children can ask about it and report back to school. Alternatively, the children can find and read books for the very young about space travel.

Investigations

Invite the children to find out the names of all the planets in the solar system as well as something about each one.

Assessment

Complex and tricky concepts are covered in this topic and it has been placed here to set the scene for later work. The most important facts that all the children should be tested on relate to safety in the sun.

Sometimes . . .

The moon looks like

The moon looks like

The moon looks like

Have you seen the moon in all these shapes?
Can you describe what you have seen?

Making noises

Learning targets

The children should be able to:

1 ➤➤ examine the range of noise that can be made by the human voice

2 ➤➤ make an instrument

3 ➤➤ identify a variety of noises

Before you start

Lesson preparation

Lesson 1

Piano accompaniment or a recording of an accompaniment to some songs the children know will be necessary in this lesson.

Lesson 2

To make their own instruments, the children require junk modelling materials, including card tubes, cartons, clean cans without sharp edges, dried pulses, milk bottle tops, rubber bands, shoe boxes, sticky tape and wire. Photocopy Copymaster 82.

Lesson 3

Before the lesson, make a tape of some sounds from round the school, including, for example, a delivery lorry reversing, school assembly, pans clattering in the school kitchen, playground noises and a telephone ringing. Collect a box of objects with which the children can make their own sound effects. Photocopy Copymaster 83.

Investigations

Make available to the children card, paper and other modelling equipment that they ask for.

Health and safety

The next topic is all about ears but in any work involving hearing and listening the children can be reminded that ears need care and loud noise can damage their ears.

Teaching the lessons

Lesson 1 ①

Vocabulary

Noise, music, voice, voice box

Introduction | 10min |

▦ Point out to the children that humans have their own instrument for making noises. This is the voice box. Allow the children to touch the front of their necks very gently while they hum. They will be able to detect where the sound is coming from. Remind the children that we make a range of noises with our voices.

Activities | 20min |

◆◆ Divide the class into groups and ask each group to make a list of as many different sounds that we make with our voices as they can.

▦ Take the whole class in a singing session, reminding the children to think about the range of sounds they are making. Point out that we use our tongue, teeth and lips in different ways to make different sounds.

Closing the lesson | 10min |

▦ Examine the group lists of sounds and create a class list of the ways humans make sounds. The list may include the following: calling out, crying, laughing, shouting, singing, whispering, whistling.

Lesson 2 ②

Vocabulary

Air, blow, guitar, instrument, pluck, scrape, strum, tap; other words associated with playing an instrument

Introduction | 10min |

▦ Talk to the children about what they understand by the words 'musical instruments'.

Activities | 25min |

👥 Allow the children to pair up. Allow all the children access to junk modelling materials so that they can make at least one instrument between two of them but preferably one each if there is time. Here are some suggestions for home-made instruments.

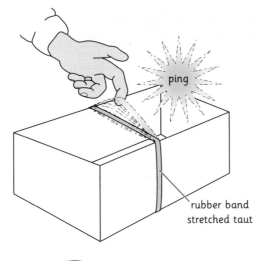

ping

rubber band
stretched taut

1 empty drum or jar

2 rice, dried peas,
lentils or pasta

3 seal lid with strong tape

4 shake away

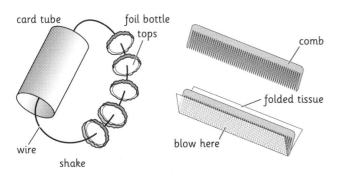

card tube

foil bottle
tops

comb

folded tissue

blow here

wire

shake

👤 Give each child a copy of **Copymaster 82** and ask them to draw the instrument that they made.

Closing the lesson 🔟min

▦ Allow the children to use their instruments to create a class-band piece.

Lesson 3 ③

Vocabulary

Hear, listen, noise, sound, sound effect

Introduction 15min

▦ Remind the children that there are sounds all round us all of which we learn to distinguish and name. Play to the children the tape of sounds recorded round the school. When they have heard it through, rewind the tape and play it again.

Activities 20min

👤 Give each child a copy of **Copymaster 83**. Ask them to list what they think the sounds on the tape are.

👥 Divide the class into groups. Invite each group to take things from the junk box and create some sound effects. If it is appropriate, give them a challenge such as, for example, to make noises like those of a thunderstorm, a football match, a car race and a birthday party.

Closing the lesson 🔟min

▦ Review the tape, checking the children's answers to the sounds on them.

After the lessons

Homework

Ask the children to take a favourite story and try making some sound effects to match part of it. Ask them to see if they can create a range of sounds using blowing, tapping, plucking and scraping.

Investigations

Invite the children to try making some toys that make a noise. The children can then work out how the noises are made. Here is an example of such a toy.

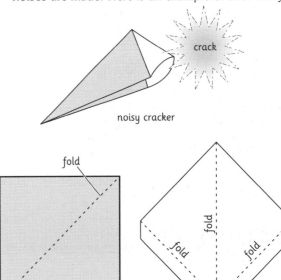

crack

noisy cracker

fold

card 7cm square

fold

fold

fold

paper 7cm square

glue in place one flap at a time
waiting for the glue to dry

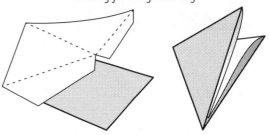

Assessment

Note the children's attention to the lesson activities to give an indication of their learning.

Hearing

Learning targets

The children should know:

1 ➡→ that hearing is one of our senses
2 ➡→ that we hear with our ears
3 ➡→ that care must be taken to look after our ears
4 ➡→ something about ears and hearing in other species

Before you start

Lesson preparation

Lesson 1

A poster or wallchart reminding the children of our five senses is required. A pair of large headphones would be useful. Each pair of children will need two empty containers like those which held gravy granules or drinking chocolate, and a piece of string. A bradawl or other sharp tool is required to make a hole in the base of each container. A washer, button or card disc is also required for each container, as shown in the lesson notes below. A length of plastic or rubber hose and two plastic funnels could also be used by the children, as shown in the lesson notes. Photocopy Copymaster 84.

Lesson 2

Photocopy Copymaster 85. The children will need poster-sized paper and art materials to produce their own posters.

Lesson 3

Books, CD-ROMs and other resources for the young about hearing in other animals are required for this lesson. Some video footage of animals is also required. These could show pets, farm animals or animals in the wild but should include species with prominent ears.

Investigations

Invite someone with a knowledge of sign language to come into school.

Health and safety

This topic is all about ears and the children should be reminded that ears need care and loud noise can damage their ears.

Teaching the lessons

Lesson 1   ① ②

Vocabulary

Earmuffs, ears, five senses, hearing, listening, outer ear, sense

Introduction | 10 min |

▓ Remind the children, using the wallchart as a resource, that we have five senses, namely, sight, hearing, smell, taste and touch. Tell the children that sensing is getting information from around you by using your senses.

Activities | 35 min |

▓ Invite a child to listen while you whisper something to them. Then ask them to don the headphones. Whisper another message without allowing them to see your lips. They may be unable to hear anything. Discuss with the children the fact that this shows that we hear using our ears. Allow several more children to try the experiment, then compare the results.

▓▓ Allow the children to pair up. Give each pair two empty containers like those which held gravy granules or drinking chocolate, and a piece of string. Make a hole in the base of each container (it might be advisable to do this before the lesson). Ask the children to make a play telephone with which they can experiment along the lines of those illustrated on the opposite page.

 Ask each child to complete **Copymaster 84**.

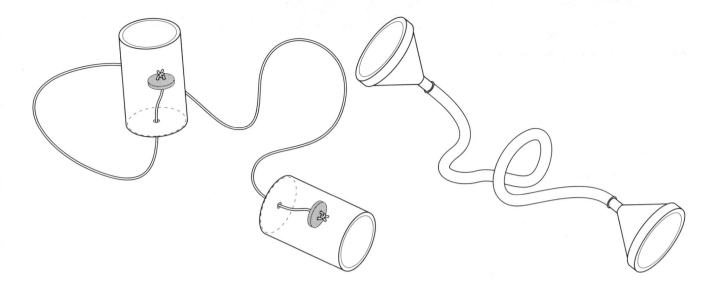

Closing the lesson | 5 min

Ask the children quick-fire questions to test what they know. Include the following:

What sense enables us to hear? (Hearing.)

What do we hear with? (Ears.)

Why is it important to be able to hear? (We can understand one another, be warned of danger.)

Lesson 2   ③

Vocabulary

Care, ears, deafness, delicate, hearing, noise

Introduction | 10 min

Talk to the children about their own experiences connected with ears; for example, hearing tests, deafness in the family, hearing aids and sign language.

Activities | 20 min

Discuss why the children should take care of their ears, using **Copymaster 85** as necessary to support the discussion.

Ask the children to create an ear-care poster.

Closing the lesson | 10 min

Mount an impromptu exhibition of the children's posters (which may be unfinished). Read aloud the messages and allow the children to choose the four most powerful ones to be displayed in a public part of the school.

Lesson 3   ④

Vocabulary

Cat, dog, ears, hearing, outer ear, rabbit, sound direction, turn; the names of animals that emerge from the sources

Introduction | 10 min

Talk to the children about their pets' ears, asking key questions such as:

How do they differ from the ears of humans?

Can they move their outer ears?

Why do they move their outer ears?

Activities | 20 min

Divide the class into groups. Give each group the chance to explore some of the resources about the ears of other animals.

Allow the children to report back on what they found. Then show them the video footage of animals, stopping the video to point out the ears.

Closing the lesson | 10 min

Review what the children have learned, confirming that other species can move their outer ears in the direction of a sound.

After the lessons

Homework

Ask the children to observe and draw a family pet with prominent ears or, with permission, they can draw one of their friend's pets. They should observe the animal over a short period of about 10 minutes, watching especially what happens to the creature's outer ears.

Investigations

Ask the children to find out more about sign language for the deaf. Invite someone with a knowledge of sign language to come and demonstrate it to the children and teach them some sign language.

Assessment

Practical work and attention to the lessons should be clues to the children's learning here.

Comparing sounds

Learning targets

The children should be able to:

1 ➤➤ recognize loud and soft sounds

2 ➤➤ recognize high and low sounds

3 ➤➤ recognize some of the sounds that animals make

Before you start

Lesson preparation

Lesson 1

It would be helpful to have some stimulus pictures and posters of things that make sounds. These may include, for example, aircraft, tugboats, a dance band, a flock of birds, trees in the wind, a road-sweeper and a town crier. Photocopy Copymaster 86.

Lesson 2

Collect about ten glass bottles and jars and set them in a row. Several jugs of water containing food colouring will be required. Three pairs of sticks with which to tap the bottles should be set

aside. The children will need piano or tape accompaniment to sing about four songs that they know.

Lesson 3

Books, CD-ROMs and other resources with information about the noises animals make would be helpful here. Photocopy Copymaster 87.

Investigations

Books, CD-ROMs and other resources for the young about sound are required.

Health and safety

As with all topics concerned with sound, the children should be reminded that ears need care and loud noise can damage their ears.

Teaching the lessons

Lesson 1 ①

Vocabulary

Low, shout, soft, sound, whisper; other words the children use in describing sounds

Introduction [10min]

▦ Use your voice to show the children that we can make loud and soft sounds. Show the children the signal you will give to stop making a sound and ask them to do the following: make as loud a sound as they can, make the quietest sound they can, make the sound of ordinary talking and make the sound of a teacher talking in assembly.

Discuss with the children the fact that we call the loudness or softness of a sound its volume. Recall some expressions we use to describe sound levels, including 'you could have heard a pin drop', 'he was as quiet as a mouse', 'there was thunderous applause'.

Activities [20min]

▦ Make a list on the board of all the sounds in a range of volumes that the children can think of. Start them off with, for example, a clap of thunder, the rattle of a tea cup, windscreen wipers on a windscreen.

👥 Ask the children to pair up. Give each pair a copy of **Copymaster 86**. Allow them time to talk about these sounds and others they know.

Closing the lesson [10min]

▦ Add to the list any additional sounds the children have thought of. Then with the children's help, try to rank according to volume.

Lesson 2 ②

Vocabulary

Low, high, sound

Introduction [10min]

▦ Speak and sing in a low voice and a high voice and ask the children to describe the difference. Invite them to make some low and high sounds with their own voices.

Activities [30min]

▦ Put about ten glass bottles and jars in a row and randomly add different amounts of coloured water to them. Tap one of the bottles. Then tap a whole series of bottles and ask the children to describe what they hear. Then tap one bottle followed by another and ask the children whether the second sound was higher or lower than the first. Do this with several bottles, placing them so that the lowest sound is produced by the jar at the left end of the row from the children's point of view. Tap out a little tune on the jars. Then allow one child to play them, followed by two children playing together.

Invite the children to think about when they are singing high and low notes during a singing lesson. Stop the song from time to time and quiz the children about particular notes.

Closing the lesson
5 min

Play, sing or speak sounds that are high and low and choose individual children to describe them.

Lesson 3
③

Vocabulary

Animal, noise, sounds; the names of particular animals and noises that are raised in the lesson

Introduction
5 min

Talk to the children about animal noise. Remind them of any information they may have gleaned in previous topics concerned with this. Discuss why they think that animals make noises. Talk about the ways animals warn each other and convey other messages. Draw the children's attention to the animal chart and talk about the sounds the animals shown may make. Below is an example chart.

Activities
20 min

Give the children a chance to examine the resources about animal noise. They can return to these in another session to find out more.

Allow the children to write what they know on **Copymaster 87**.

Closing the lesson
10 min

Establish that animal sounds can be loud and soft, high and low and that they serve to convey messages just as the noises we make with our voices do.

After the lessons

Homework

Ask the children to find the tune they like playing best on the recorder or the song they like singing best and talk to their family or the class about which parts are loud and soft, high and low.

Investigations

Ask the children to find out what a decibel is and the range of decibels commonly predicted for a range of sounds.

Assessment

Children may vary in their discriminatory powers regarding sound but the distinctions made in these lessons should be understood by all the children.

Down on the farm. What noises do these animals make?

What makes a sound?

Learning targets

The children should be able to:

1 ➤➤ talk about how a recorder works
2 ➤➤ compare the recorder with other classroom instruments
3 ➤➤ observe instruments while they are played
4 ➤➤ talk about what moves when musical instruments are played
5 ➤➤ understand the word vibration

Before you start

Lesson preparation

Lesson 1

The recorder has been chosen as the instrument for investigation in this lesson because it is widely used in schools. As many as possible should be available for the lesson. If there is another suitable instrument available it can be used instead. You can use a demonstration instrument if the children do not routinely have access to instruments.

Have available some instruments for a class band. These might include, for example, bells, chime bars, coconut shells, cymbals, glockenspiels, maracas, shakers, sticks, tambourines, tambours and triangles. A class music table is illustrated in the lesson notes on the opposite page.

Lesson 2

A range of instruments, along with people who can play them, are required. Here are some suggestions: glockenspiel or chime bars, guitar, piano, recorder and wind and brass instruments if available. Photocopy Copymaster 88.

Lesson 3

A wooden ruler and a heavy book are needed. Photocopy Copymaster 89. Some example instruments from the following are required for the session: bells, chime bars, coconut shells, cymbals, glockenspiels, maracas, shakers, sticks, tambourines, tambours and triangles.

Investigations

Books, CD-ROMs and other sources of information about the instruments of the orchestra are needed.

Health and safety

As with all topics concerned with sound, the children should be reminded that ears need care and loud noise can damage their ears.

Teaching the lessons

Lesson 1 ① ②

Vocabulary

Air, blow, high, hole, loud, low, note, recorder, soft, sound; the names of other instruments in the class band which may include bells, chime bars, coconut shells, cymbals, glockenspiels, maracas and shakers, sticks, tambourines, tambours, triangles

Introduction 15min

▓ Show the children the parts of the recorder. Point out that it is made of wood or plastic and has a mouthpiece. Indicate the holes and show how the instrument should be held. Ask the children a series of probing questions about the recorder. They may include the following:

How de we get a sound out of this instrument?

What is being blown into it?

What happens when the holes are uncovered?

What happens when they are covered?

To what does covering a hole make a difference?

How are high notes produced?

How are low notes produced?

Activities 20min

♣ Divide the class into groups. Give each group a different instrument from the class collection. Ask them to determine how it is played, where the sound comes from and how it differs from a recorder. Opposite is an example class music collection.

Play along
with the tape

Tap out
these
rhythms
.../...

Make a
sound
like a ...

Rhythms
to
play

Songs
to sing

Come and
sit and play

▦ Ask the children, a group at a time, to compare and contrast their instrument with a recorder.

Closing the lesson [5 min]

▦ Point out that different instruments are blown, shaken or tapped to obtain a sound.

Lesson 2 ③ ④

Vocabulary

Air, blow, guitar, instrument, piano, pluck, recorder, scrape, shake, strum, tap; the names of other instruments shown to the children, along with words associated with playing an instrument

Introduction [15 min]

▦ Invite musicians to show their instruments to the children and to play them in front of the class.

Activities [25 min]

▦ Ask the children what they noticed about how the instruments were played. Check that they understand that sounds are produced in a variety of ways.

👤 Ask each child to complete **Copymaster 88**. If the instruments depicted are not among those demonstrated to the children, the appropriate ones should be added.

Closing the lesson [5 min]

▦ Review the children's understanding of how instruments are played.

Lesson 3 ⑤

Vocabulary

Instrument, sound, vibration

Introduction [5 min]

▦ Review the work the children have done involving musical instruments by asking them what they know about how sounds are produced. They should indicate that something moves to make a sound.

Activities [25 min]

▦ Place the wooden ruler at the edge of a table, so that about one-third of it extends beyond the table edge. Anchor it with a heavy book. Press down on the book with one hand while bending the ruler with the other. When released, the ruler will move and emit a sound. Try this several times so that the children have the chance to hear the sound clearly. Then move the ruler so that more of it extends beyond the table edge. When bent and released it will emit a different sound. Try this several times. Explain that this regular back and forth movement is necessary to make a sound and is called a vibration.

👤 Give the children time to describe on **Copymaster 89** the experiment they have just watched.

Closing the lesson [5 min]

▦ Allow volunteers to take an instrument from the music table and see if they can feel what is vibrating when a noise comes from the instrument.

After the lessons

Homework

Give the children a music/sound quiz sheet. It could include some of the following: pictures of instruments to name, a picture of a tuning fork to name, notes on a stave for the children to say whether they are high or low.

Investigations

Ask the children to find out about an instrument from the orchestra that they have not met in the lessons. Give them a short list of challenges, including:

How is the sound made?

Can the instrument be played loudly and softly?

Can mostly high notes or mostly low notes be played on this instrument?

What parts of the instrument move when a sound is made?

Assessment

Review the children's written work and involvement in practical work in class.

Sound travelling

Learning targets

The children should be able to:

1 ➤➤ say that sound travels
2 ➤➤ test whether sound gets fainter as it travels from its source
3 ➤➤ say what soundproofing is
4 ➤➤ say something about echoes

Before you start

Lesson preparation

Lesson 1

The children will need to go into the hall at the beginning of the lesson. Bring with you a tape recorder and a tape with music on it. The children will need access to as large a space as possible, such as the playground if this is extensive or the playing field. Trundle wheels or surveyor's tape may be required. Photocopy Copymaster 90.

Lesson 2

If possible, the children should have access to a music room or a room with some sort of soundproofing. A clock with a loud tick, a large box and plenty of cushion wadding or polystyrene tiles will also be required. Photocopy Copymaster 91.

Lesson 3

Books, CD-ROMs and other resources about bats, dolphins and other creatures that use echo-sounding are needed.

Investigations

Books, CD-ROMs and other secondary resources about bats, dolphins and other creatures that use echo-sounding are needed.

Health and safety

As with all topics concerned with sound, the children should be reminded that ears need care and loud noise can damage their ears.

Teaching the lessons

Lesson 1 ① ②

Vocabulary

Detect, fainter, source, sound, travel, volume

Introduction ⌜10 min⌟

▨ Take the children into the hall for the introduction to the lesson, taking with you a tape recorder and a music tape. Allow the children to gather round and listen to the music with the volume control quite low. Then allow the children to disperse to the walls of the hall and listen there. Ask them what they notice about the volume. Tell them that they are going to be testing out their ideas.

Activities ⌜30 min⌟

 Divide the class into groups. Take the children into the playground or to playing field. Ask one child in each group to be the caller, while the others, in a line, gradually move away from the person who is the source of the noise. This could, for example, be a blast on a whistle, a shout or a tap on some sticks. The children can suggest ways to measure and collect information. They may choose to measure distance in paces or strides or use a trundle wheel or surveyor's tape. Here are some suggested challenges:

Does the sound get fainter?

At what distance does it stop being clear?

Is there a distance at which it cannot be heard at all?

👤 Ask the children to write up the experiment they have done on **Copymaster 90**.

Closing the lesson ⌜5 min⌟

▨ Discuss and compare the results of the children's experiments.

Lesson 2

Vocabulary

Sound, soundproof, travel

Introduction `10 min`

 Show the children any special areas of the school where the structure allows sound levels to be reduced. This could include carpeted areas, library corners and music rooms. Ask the children what they can see that might reduce the noise levels.

Activities `25 min`

 Ask the children to say why it may be important to stop sound travelling. Point out that in some places it is important to have quiet, for example, examination rooms, radio and television stations, and recording studios. Mention the fact that we sometimes do not want to be disturbed by sound coming from within a room, for example, the music room.

Tell the children that when such a room is built so that sounds do not travel outside it this is called soundproofed. Show the children the box and tell them that you are going to show them how soundproofing works. Allow them to listen to the ticking clock for a few moments. Place the clock in the box and put the lid on. The ticking will still be heard (it may even sound louder than when outside the box). Take the clock out of the box and line the box on all its surfaces with thick wadding or polystyrene tiles. Ask the children to predict what they think will happen to the sound of the ticking when it is placed in the box. Test out their predictions. The ticking should sound fainter.

Give each child a copy of **Copymaster 91** so that they can write about the experiment just demonstrated to them.

Closing the lesson `10 min`

Select some of the children's records of the experiment to discuss with them. Point out where in the description of the experiment the account of what was done and the account of what happened should written. Talk about how scientists usually write up their experiments.

Lesson 3

Vocabulary

Echo, bounce, sound

Introduction `10 min`

Talk to the children about their own experiences of echoes. They may have been in a subway, under a bridge or in the mountains and heard and made echoes.

Activities `20 min`

Take the children round the school buildings to see if echoes can be obtained. Sometimes an echo can be obtained in a stairwell, between buildings or even in the empty hall.

 Divide the class into groups. Give the children the chance to find out more about echoes from the classroom resources.

Closing the lesson `10 min`

Draw the children's attention to a display about echoes and ask them to add their work to it. Here is an example display.

After the lessons

Homework

Ask the children to test which room in their house is most soundproof. They should plan and carry out an experiment and report back to the class. For example, they may choose to play a radio or music tape in every room in their home while standing outside the room with the door closed.

Investigations

Invite the children to find out about bats and how they use sounds and echoes to fly safely at night. Get them to look for other animals that make use of echoes for navigation and to locate food, for example, the dolphin.

Assessment

Look at the children's written work and their participation in the lessons for clues to their learning.

Things I do.

I eat

I _____

I _____

I _____

Draw in some non-living things.

| **Living** | **Non-living** |

Join the words
to the pictures

move

grow

breathe

eat

go to
the lavatory

© Nelson Thornes 2001

We are alike

We are all alike because we have:
(colour in the parts we have)

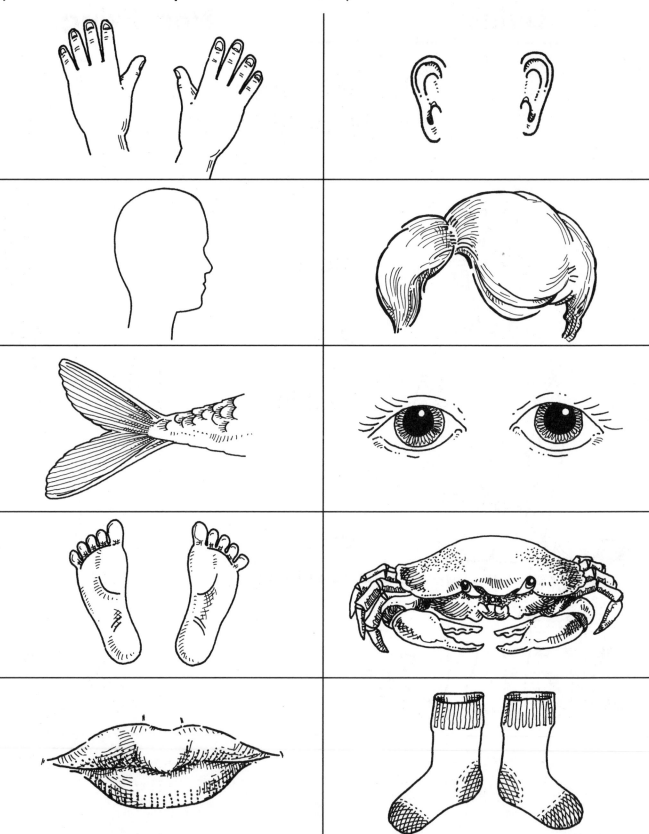

Mix and match features

© Nelson Thornes 2001

Our senses

Which sense do we use?

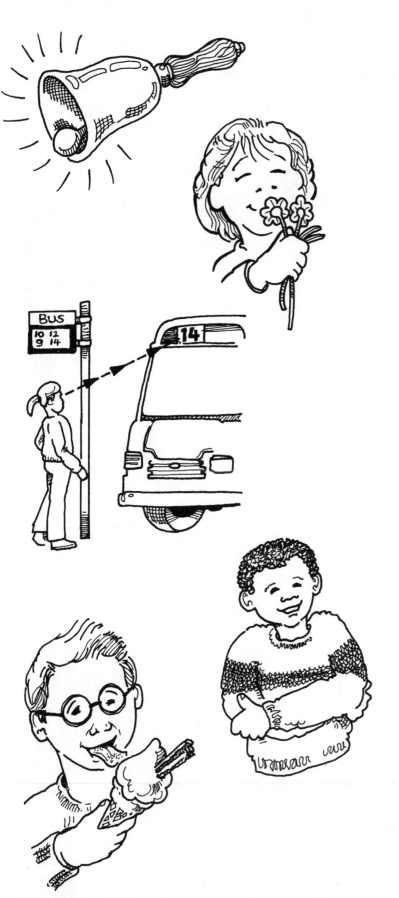

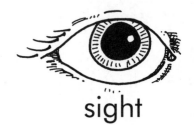

touch

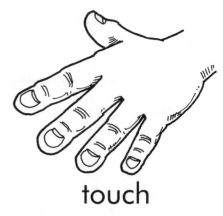

sight

hearing

taste

smell

© Nelson Thornes 2001

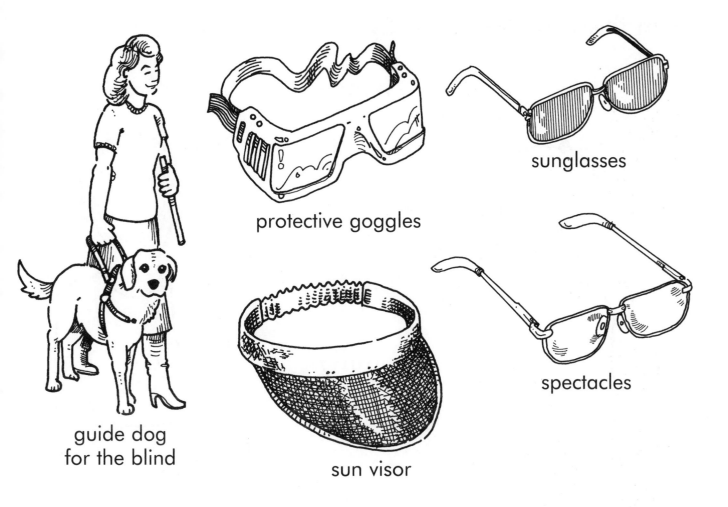

protective goggles

sunglasses

guide dog
for the blind

sun visor

spectacles

1. Someone who cannot see is _____ .

2. Guide dogs help the _____ .

3. We can wear _____ in the sun.

4. Some people need help to see well.
   They wear _____ .

5. A welder wears _____ .

6. We see with our _____ .

© Nelson Thornes 2001

Join the word to the body part.

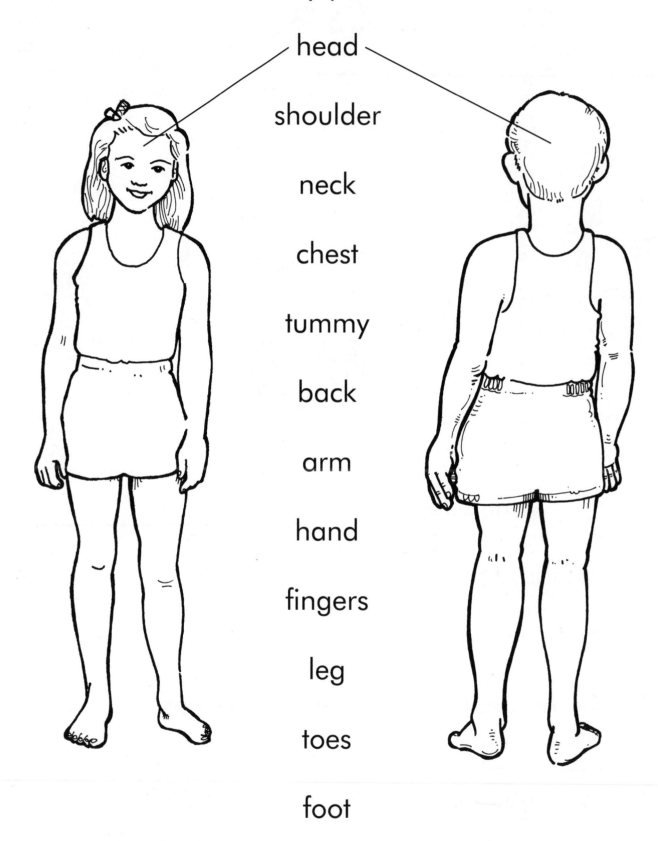

head

shoulder

neck

chest

tummy

back

arm

hand

fingers

leg

toes

foot

© Nelson Thornes 2001

Write in the missing words.

Tom's _____

Tom's _____

Tom's _____

Tom's _____

Tom's _____

Tom's _____

Tom's _____

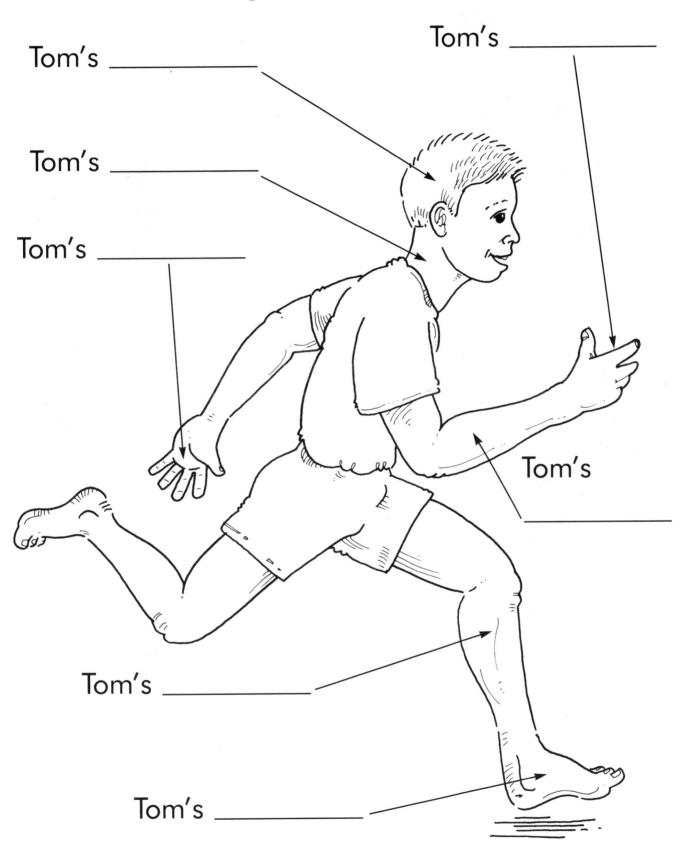

© Nelson Thornes 2001

Match the babies to the adults. Colour the pictures so that they match real animals.

© Nelson Thornes 2001

 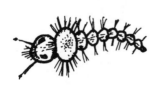 

© Nelson Thornes 2001

Foods

All these foods are good for us. Talk about which build our bodies, give us energy, keep us healthy.

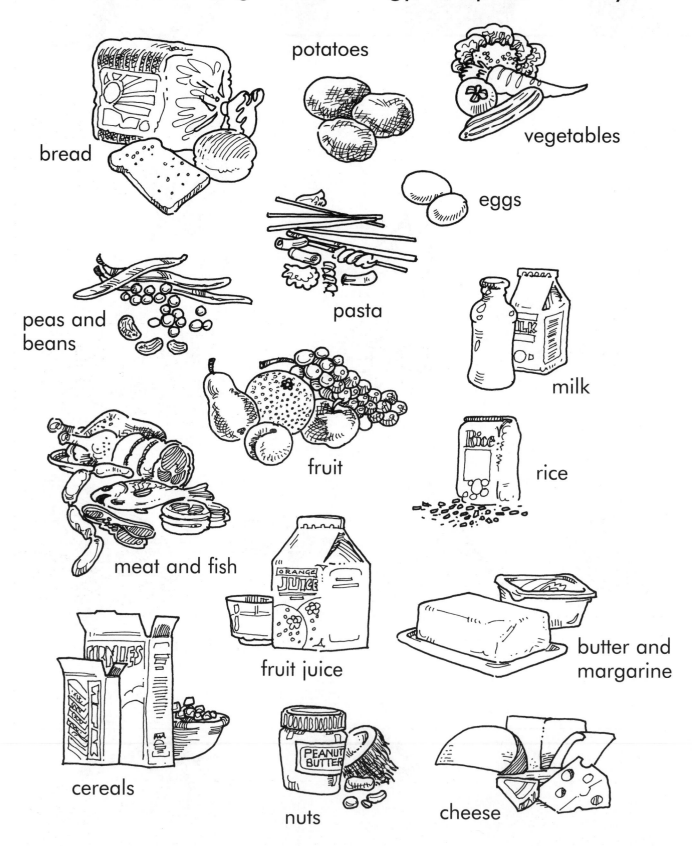

bread

potatoes

vegetables

eggs

pasta

peas and beans

milk

fruit

rice

meat and fish

fruit juice

butter and margarine

cereals

nuts

cheese

© Nelson Thornes 2001

Draw the animal	Draw the animal
Grass and leaves / Meat or fish / All kinds of food	Grass and leaves / Meat or fish / All kinds of food
Draw the animal	Draw the animal
Grass and leaves / Meat or fish / All kinds of food	Grass and leaves / Meat or fish / All kinds of food
Draw the animal	Draw the animal
Grass and leaves / Meat or fish / All kinds of food	Grass and leaves / Meat or fish / All kinds of food
Draw the animal	Draw the animal
Grass and leaves / Meat or fish / All kinds of food	Grass and leaves / Meat or fish / All kinds of food

© Nelson Thornes 2001

Caring for ill people

Tom is not well. Draw Tom in bed. Draw in things to show Tom is cared for so that he gets better.

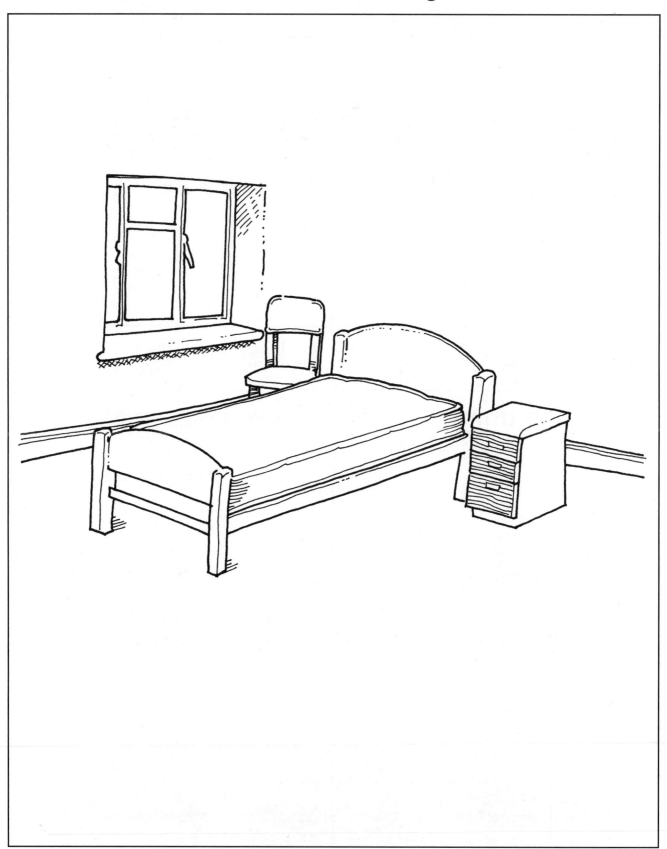

Warning signs

Colour all the signs in yellow.

- fold back

Danger   Harmful   Irritant

Corrosive   Highly Flammable   Toxic

© Nelson Thornes 2001

Pet	How many people have a . . . . . ?

Draw another pet.

Pet	How many people have a . . . . . ?
No pets	

© Nelson Thornes 2001

Talk about which animals do each of these things.

eat	grow	drink
fly	swim	jump
roll over	groom	breathe
bark	chase	live underwater
peck	scratch	hop
live in the air	have babies	chew
excrete	move	see

© Nelson Thornes 2001

Discovering mini-beasts

Draw the pictures to
finish the story.

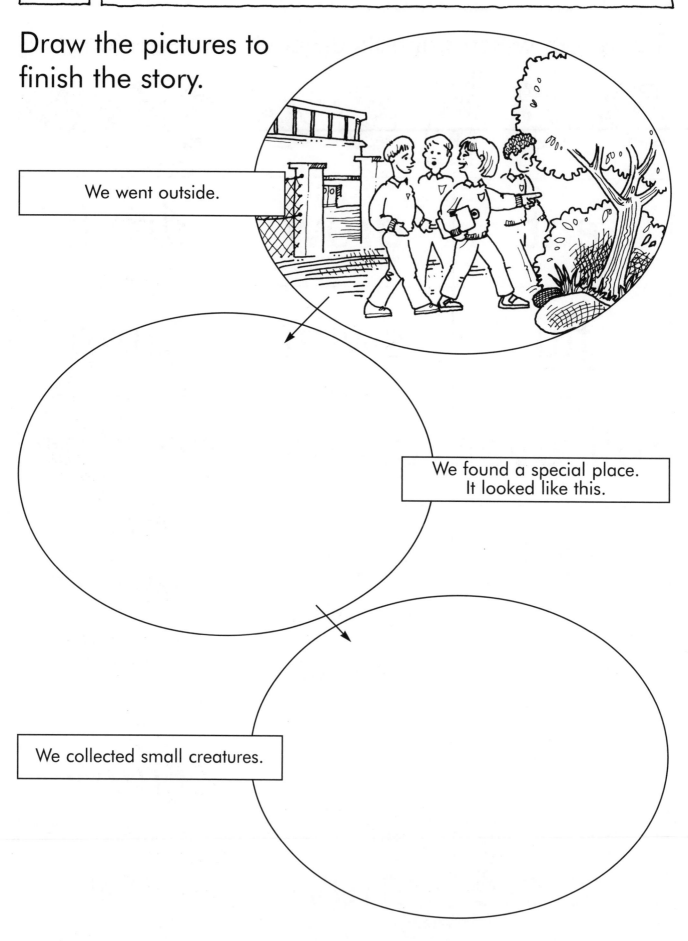

We went outside.

We found a special place.
It looked like this.

We collected small creatures.

© Nelson Thornes 2001

Use this to spot some of the creatures you have seen.

woodlouse

centipede

millipede

ladybird

ant

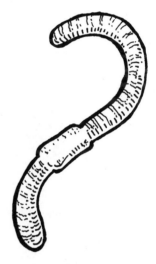

earthworm

aphid

earwig

snail

garden spider

© Nelson Thornes 2001

Inside our bodies we each have a skeleton made of bones.

Muscles are joined to the bones.

We are able to move because we have muscles.

Draw yourself on the move and using your muscles.

© Nelson Thornes 2001

Different animals move in different ways. Choose an animal and draw how it moves.

Talk about your pictures.

© Nelson Thornes 2001

Fruits and vegetables

Which of these fruits and vegetables do you like eating? Make a list. Say whether they grow above or below ground.

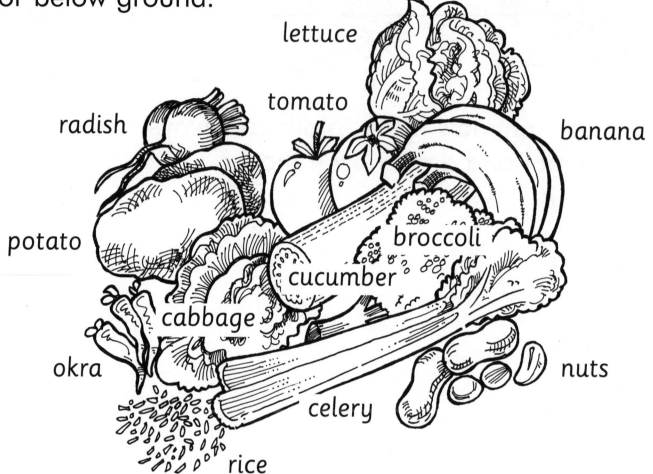

Name of fruit or vegetable	Above or below ground?

© Nelson Thornes 2001

Plants

plants drink | plants have babies

plants grow | plants need food

© Nelson Thornes 2001

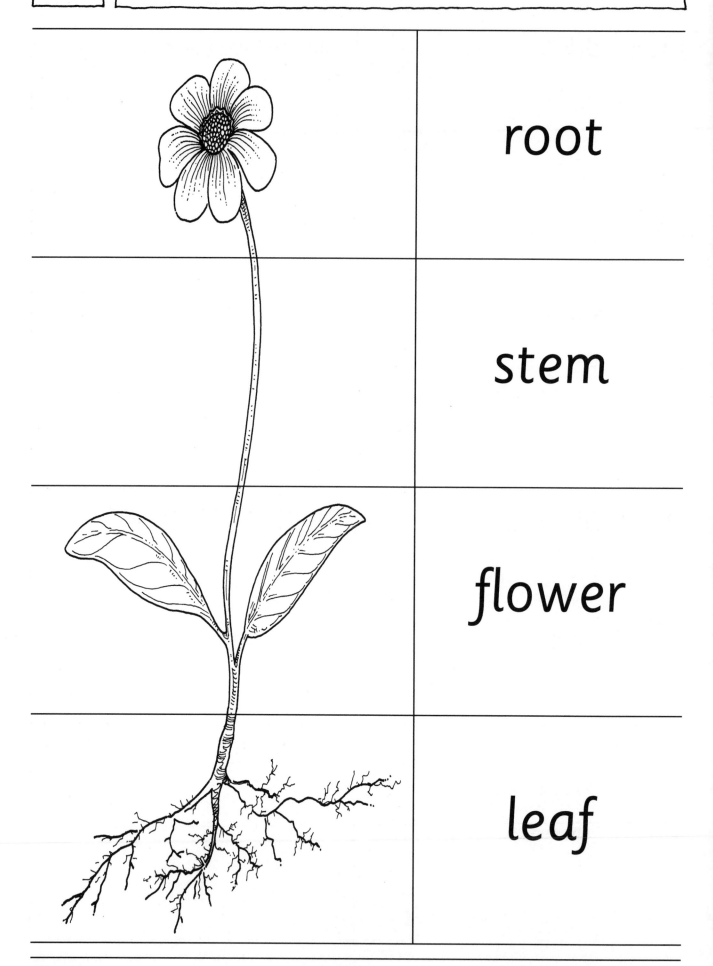

root

stem

flower

leaf

© Nelson Thornes 2001

Identifying parts of plants

	Draw	Write
Plant 1	I can see	It is the
Plant 2	I can see	It is the
Plant 3	I can see	It is the
Plant 4	I can see	It is the

© Nelson Thornes 2001

25 | Growing plants

Draw how you think the plants will look.

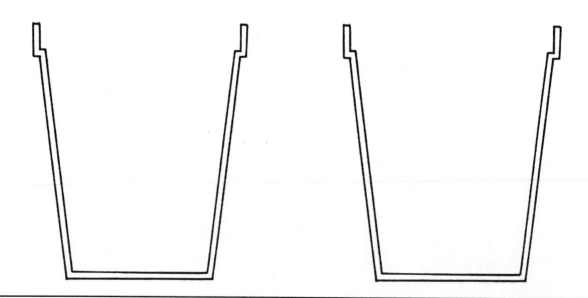

© Nelson Thornes 2001

26 | **What plants need**

What do plants need? Tick (✔). Colour in.

water

warmth

light

soft toy

soil or
compost

ice cream

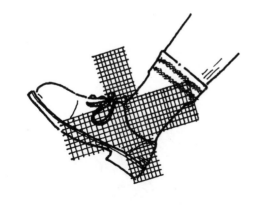

care

umbrella

© Nelson Thornes 2001

Draw in the seeds you see.

tomato

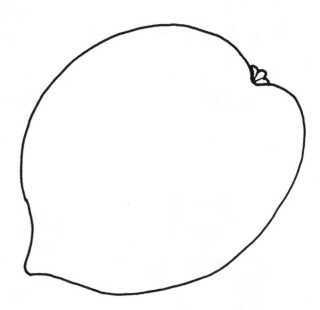

plum, peach or
nectarine

strawberry

dandelion

© Nelson Thornes 2001

Life cycle of a plant

Draw three different plant lives.

seed	young plant	full-grown plant

© Nelson Thornes 2001

© Nelson Thornes 2001

129

© Nelson Thornes 2001

31 Flowers

Things to think about when looking at flowers.

What colour are they?

Red

Blue

Yellow

or . . . . . ?

What size are they?

Very small

Very large

What shape are they?

Bell

Where are they found?

Hedge   Woods   Grassland   Park or garden   Hills

When do they flower?

Spring   Summer   Autumn   Winter

© Nelson Thornes 2001

Can you find leaves like these?

© Nelson Thornes 2001

Sense organs

Whose nose?

 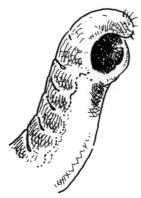 

Whose ears?

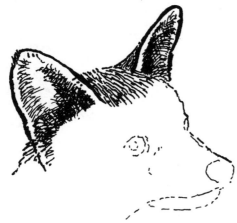 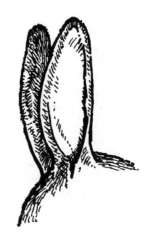

Whose eyes?

 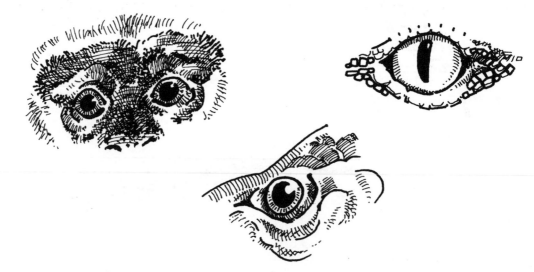

© Nelson Thornes 2001

Name of animal

Colours

What is it like?

(Some words to help you: fur, face, nose, ears, eyes, legs, paws, tail)

What else do you know about this animal?

133

© Nelson Thornes 2001

Fishy facts

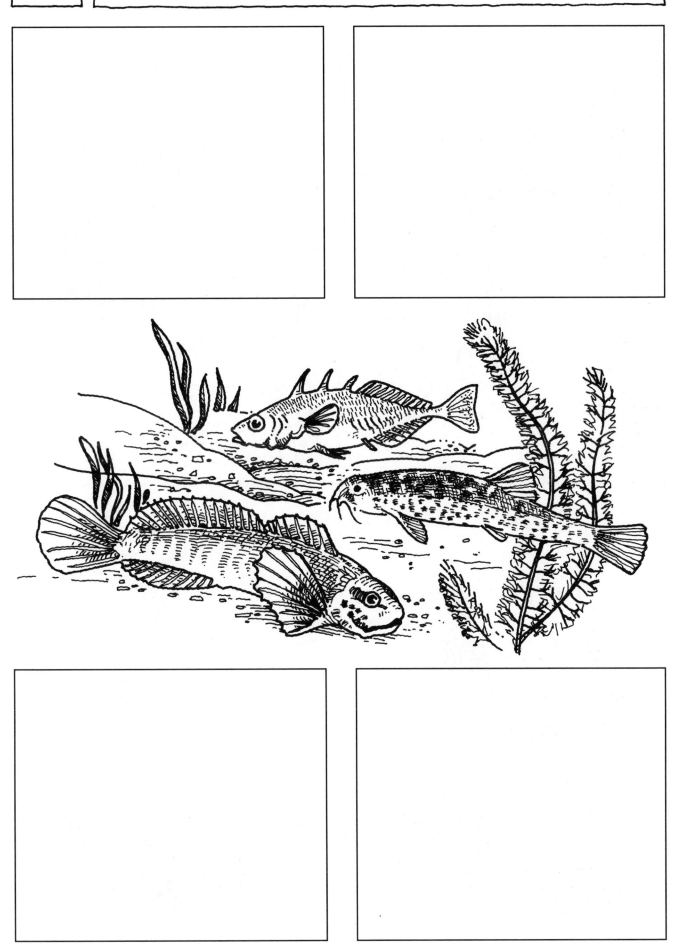

© Nelson Thornes 2001

© Nelson Thornes 2001

I saw

I heard

I wrote about

I drew

I <u>now</u> know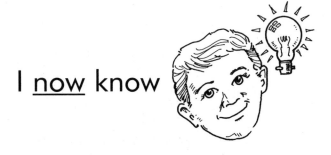

© Nelson Thornes 2001

What materials feel like

Draw and write how the materials feel.

Draw	Write

Draw	Write

Draw	Write

© Nelson Thornes 2001

Draw and name some materials that go together.

Why did you put them together?

I put them together because _____

_____

_____

© Nelson Thornes 2001

Magnetic fish

One of these (card strip)

Eight paper clips

Two of these

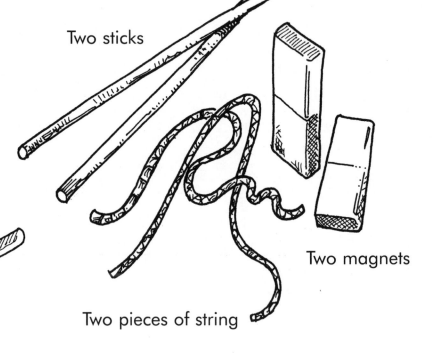

Two sticks

Two magnets

Two pieces of string

Two pairs of scissors

1. Draw and colour the underwater scene on the card strip.
2. Draw and cut out four fish each.
3. Fix a paper clip to each fish.
4. Tie string to magnet and stick.
5. Make up 'aquarium'.
6. Put in fish.
7. Go fishing!

© Nelson Thornes 2001

Test and tick (✔) those attracted to the magnet.

wax crayon	ribbon	button	paper fastener	2p coin
paper	chalk	rubber band	cork	marble
paper clip	eraser	card	pebble	ring
clothes peg	string	leaf	plastic	pencil
pottery flower pot	wood	scissors	bottle top	feather
screw	door handle	food tin	lunchbox	key

© Nelson Thornes 2001

I can see clearly through...	I can see through but not clearly...
I can see only a little through...	I can see nothing through...

© Nelson Thornes 2001

Around the school try to look **through** things. Draw some of the things that belong in each group below.

I can see clearly through...

_____

I cannot see clearly through...

_____

I cannot see through at all...

These are made of wood

These are made of plastic

These are made of metal

© Nelson Thornes 2001

Draw the things that go together like this.

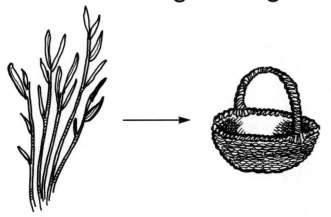

© Nelson Thornes 2001

What is it made from? Join up.

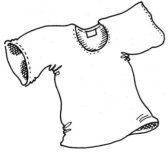

scissors

table

hairbrush

tee shirt

knife

cotton

wool

paper

metal

plastic

wood

clay

tea towel

teapot

rail ticket

flower pot

bootee

© Nelson Thornes 2001

© Nelson Thornes 2001

What would you choose to make these from and why?

swimming trunks

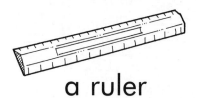

a ruler

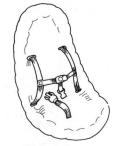

a baby harness

a cooking pot

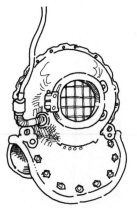

a diver's helmet

© Nelson Thornes 2001

Changing shape

Draw your lump of clay or dough.

Now draw your model to show the changes in shape you made to the clay or dough.

© Nelson Thornes 2001

Write about what happens to the shapes here.

 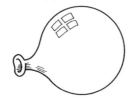 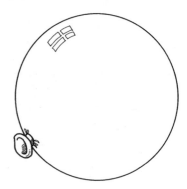

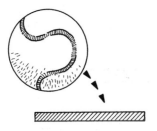 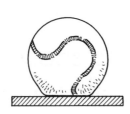 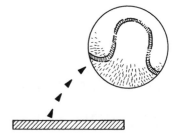

© Nelson Thornes 2001

Draw and write.

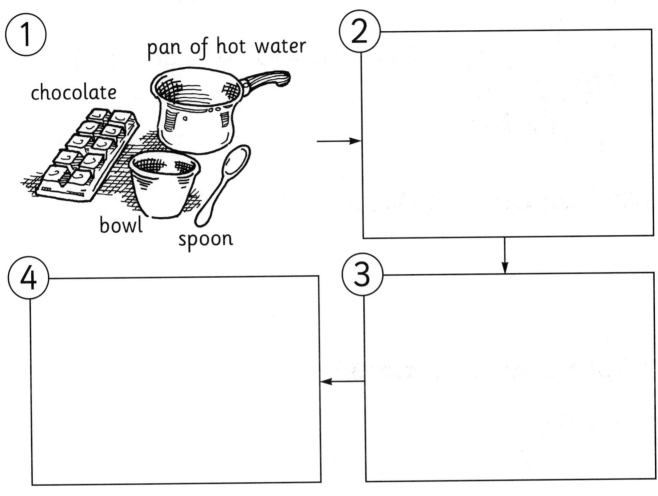

① chocolate   pan of hot water

bowl   spoon

②

③

④

Draw a picture trail to show the jelly experiment.

© Nelson Thornes 2001

Write about your experiment.

What did you try to find out?

What equipment did you use?

What did you actually do?

What happened?

Did your experiment work? How could you improve it?

© Nelson Thornes 2001

Draw and write.

Bread	Toast

How did it change? _____

_____

Raw egg	Cooked egg

How did it change? _____

_____

© Nelson Thornes 2001

This is what we need to use:

This is what we did.

Differences

Cake mixture before cooking | Cake mixture after cooking

© Nelson Thornes 2001

Write in some of the dangers here.

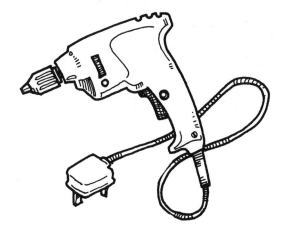

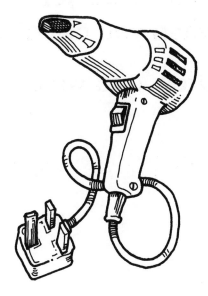

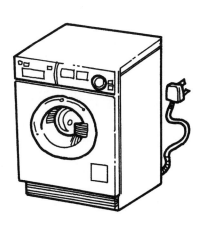

© Nelson Thornes 2001

57 | Electricity at home and at work

Ask four grown-ups you know:
'Where do you use electricity
when you are at work?'

Draw and write.

© Nelson Thornes 2001

Do you think these devices use mains electricity or batteries? Write in <u>mains</u> or <u>battery</u> and colour the mains devices red and the battery devices green.

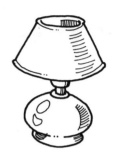
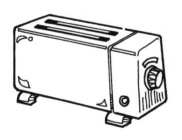

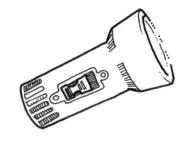

© Nelson Thornes 2001

Draw or write. What things do these when they are switched on?

Give out Light

© Nelson Thornes 2001

Draw the circuit the teacher made. The battery is drawn for you.

With the lamp <u>off</u>

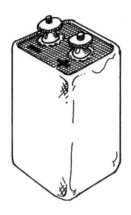

With the lamp <u>on</u>

© Nelson Thornes 2001

Draw the circuit you made. Put in the battery, buzzer or bell and switch (if you had one).

Tick (✔) which of these has a buzzer that is buzzing.

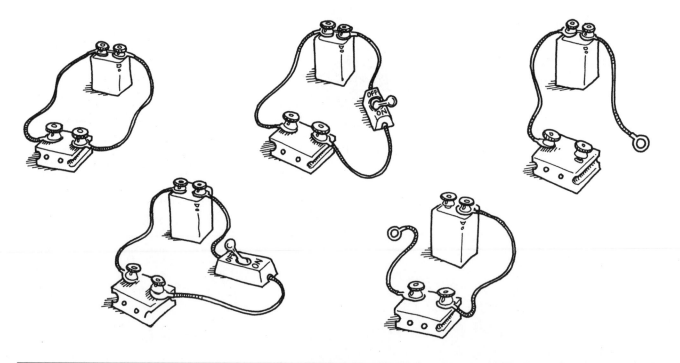

© Nelson Thornes 2001

A robot with light-up eyes

A house with a doorbell

A tree with a star light

A lighthouse

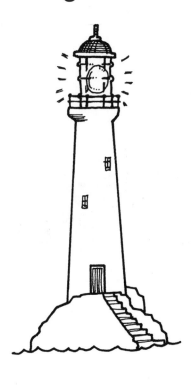

A monster or ghost with light eyes

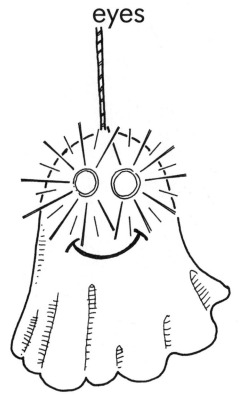

64 | Moving toys

Draw one of the toys you have worked with, showing how it can move.

© Nelson Thornes 2001

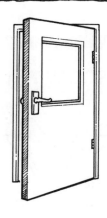

Around the classroom **push** and **pull**.
We **pull** open the door.

Draw some more places where we
push or **pull**.

© Nelson Thornes 2001

Using a bicycle

Where do we **push**? Where do we **pull**?

© Nelson Thornes 2001

Tick (✔) and talk about.
What makes the ball travel faster?

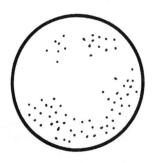

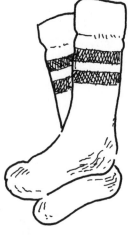

more force
in the kick

softer ball

stripy socks

Tick (✔) and talk about.
What makes the ball change direction?

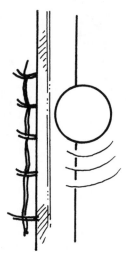

the grass

when the ball
hits something

when the
ball is stopped
and kicked

© Nelson Thornes 2001

Play marbles

Draw pictures to show what you found out when playing marbles.

Which of these tell us about crossing the road safely? Tick (✓) and talk about what they mean.

It is not safe to cross by parked cars.

It is not safe to cross when you cannot see the traffic.

It is better to use a crossing but you must still wait for the traffic to stop.

It is important to look all around when crossing the road.

It is important to listen before crossing the road.

It is important to look and listen while crossing the road.

Dogs must be on a lead near a road.

There is danger in playing ball near a road.

© Nelson Thornes 2001

Talk about these:

 Cars are heavy and made of metal.

The traffic goes fast.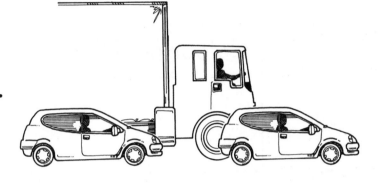

 Even when the driver puts the brake on, a car goes on moving a long way.

Cars cannot stop as soon as a driver presses the brake.

 Bikes, scooters and motorcycles are dangerous too.

You cannot be sure that a driver will let you cross in front of him or her until the car has stopped.

© Nelson Thornes 2001

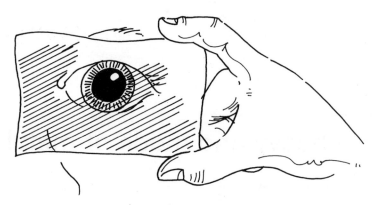

What happens to the colours?

Colour	Colour of cellophane	Colour change?
red		
blue		
yellow		
white		
black		
green		

© Nelson Thornes 2001

Talk about shiny things and reflections.

Write about what you did.

Learning Targets: Science Key Stage 1
© Nelson Thornes 2001

Draw and write.

Light and shadow

Draw some faces. Use a pencil to put in the shadows.

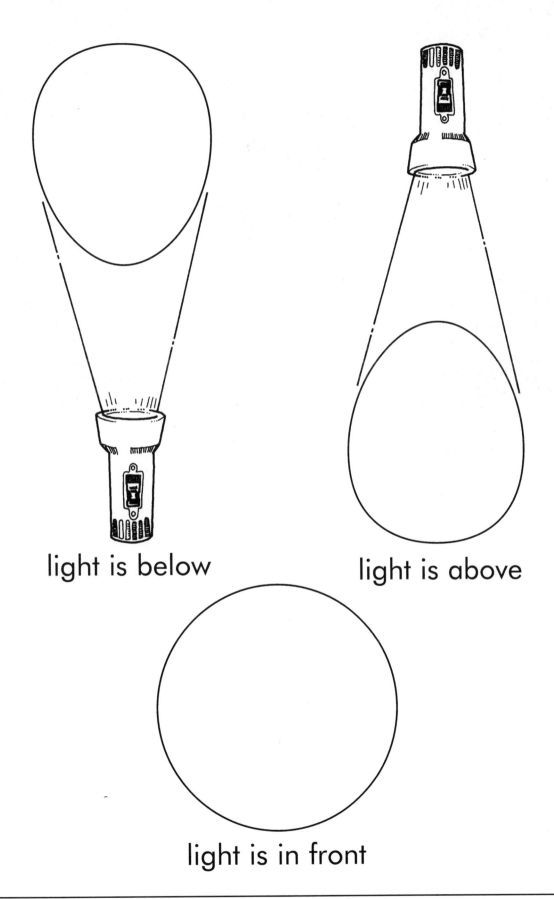

light is below

light is above

light is in front

© Nelson Thornes 2001

Shadows

Draw some shadow shapes you made.

© Nelson Thornes 2001

Making shadows

Draw the things that belonged to the shadows.

Learning Targets: Science Key Stage 1

© Nelson Thornes 2001

Finding shadows

Where can you usually see shadows in your home?

Describe some of them and put a star ✱ against the one you are going to draw round.

© Nelson Thornes 2001

Lighting in the past

candle

oil lamp

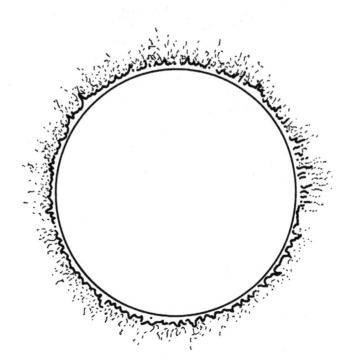

the sun

© Nelson Thornes 2001

Using light

How do these people use lights in their work?
Draw where the light goes and colour the pictures.

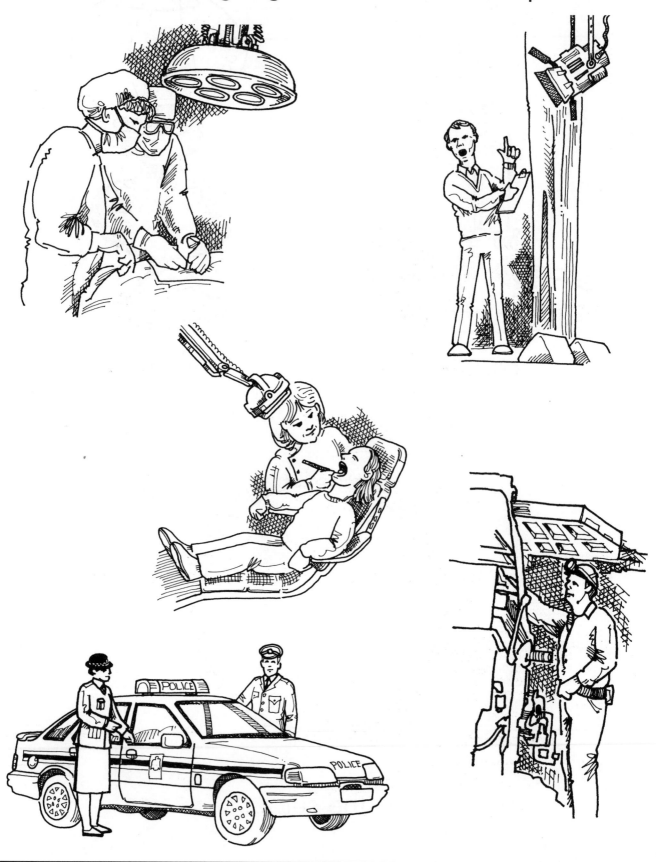

© Nelson Thornes 2001

Write what you know.

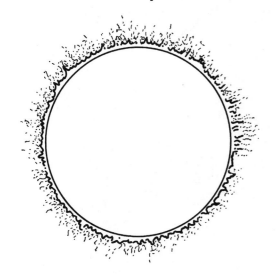

The sun

The sun's light

Safety in the sun

© Nelson Thornes 2001

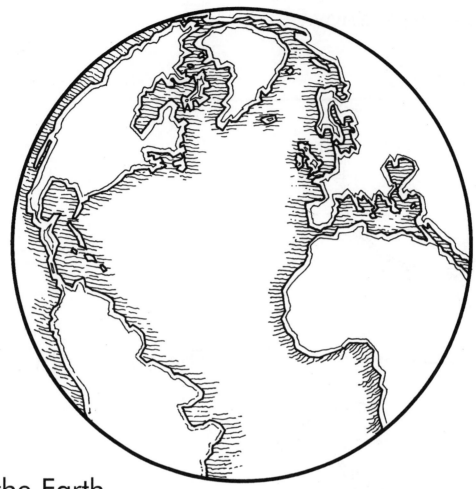

About the Earth

It is a planet ✓
It goes round the sun ✓
It has a satellite called the moon ✓

What else do you know about planet Earth?

© Nelson Thornes 2001

Make a musical instrument

Draw the instrument you made.

Write about how it is made to work.

bottle-top
shakers

bands to
strum

wooden
clackers

dried-pea
shaker

© Nelson Thornes 2001

Identifying sounds

What do you think the sounds on tape are?

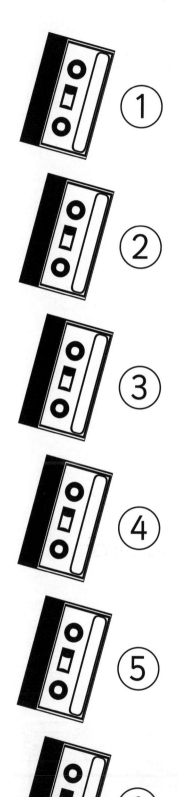

© Nelson Thornes 2001

Telephones and sound

Draw your play telephone.

How does it work?

Does it work better with the string or hose straight and taut or floppy and slack?

© Nelson Thornes 2001

© Nelson Thornes 2001

Different sounds

whisper

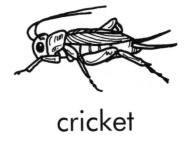

cricket

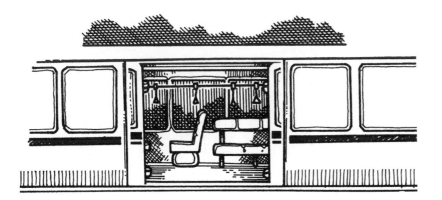

undergound train

town crier

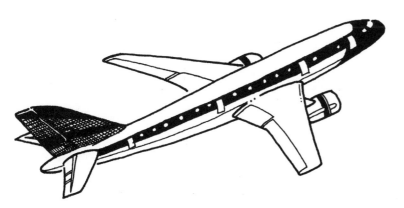

aircraft taking off

© Nelson Thornes 2001

Animals make noises. Write what you know about why they make noises.

© Nelson Thornes 2001

Musical instruments

What do you do to make a sound?

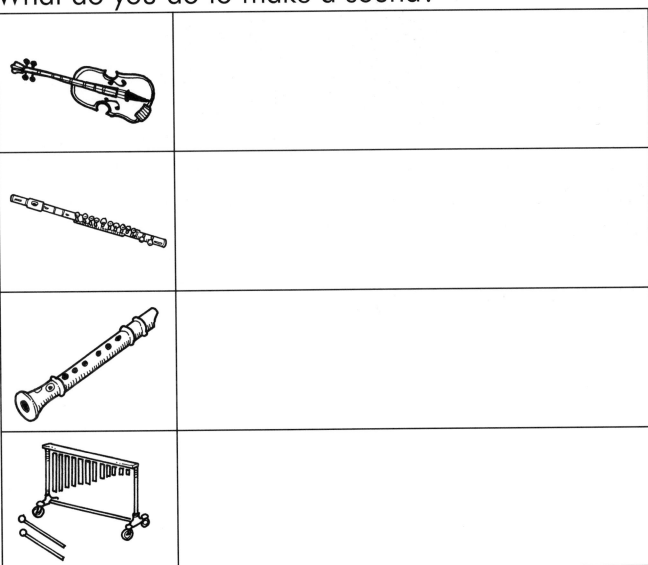

Draw and write about two more instruments.

© Nelson Thornes 2001

Making sounds

Draw pictures to show what was done to the ruler.

Describe what happened.

How do you explain what happened?

188

© Nelson Thornes 2001

My experiment with sound

Write about the experiment you did. Think about what you were finding out about, what was done and what happened.

Making sound quieter

Number the pictures.

Write about what happened.

How could the box be made more soundproof?

© Nelson Thornes 2001

RECORD SHEET 1

Name _____ Class/Year _____ Teacher's initials _____

Section	Topic		Performance in relation to learning targets	Summary remarks
Life processes and living things	1	Being alive		
	2	You and me		
	3	Our senses		
	4	Body labels		
	5	Babies		
	6	Food		
	7	Being ill, getting better		
	8	Pets		
	9	Mini-beasts		
	10	Get moving!		
	11	What is a plant?		
	12	Plant labels		
	13	Let's grow		
	14	Plant babies		
	15	Matching alike/unlike		
	16	Looking at plants		
	17	Looking at animals		
	18	Grouping		
	19	Habitats		

Learning Targets: Science Key Stage 1
RECORD SHEET 2

Name _____ Class/Year _____ Teacher's initials _____

Section		Topic	Performance in relation to learning targets	Summary remarks
Materials and their properties	20	Sensing		
	21	Is it magnetic or non-magnetic?		
	22	Transparency and other properties		
	23	Naming materials		
	24	What do we use it for?		
	25	Shape changes		
	26	Heating and cooling: changing back		
	27	Heating and cooling: all change		
Physical processes	28	Play safe		
	29	What does electricity make things do?		
	30	Making circuits		
	31	On the move		
	32	Push and pull		
	33	Speeding up, slowing down or changing direction		
	34	Road safety		
	35	Light toys		
	36	Light and darkness		
	37	Shadow play		
	38	Light sources		
	39	The sun, the Earth and the moon		
	40	Making noises		
	41	Hearing		
	42	Comparing sounds		
	43	What makes a sound?		
	44	Sound travelling		